CHRONICLES OF A KINGDOM

By the same author:

Beauty from Ashes (Bible Reading Fellowship)
Beyond Healing (Hodder & Stoughton)
Broken Stone (Pickering & Inglis)
The Firebrand (Marshall Pickering)
Fragile Dreams (Marshall Pickering)
God's Gloves (Marshall Pickering)
Leaning On a Spider's Web (Hodder & Stoughton)
No Hands But Ours (HarperCollins)
Turning Point (Hodder & Stoughton)
Unexpected Healing (Hodder & Stoughton)
Where Have You Gone, God? (Hodder & Stoughton)
Who Do You Say I am? (Hodder & Stoughton)

Chronicles of a Kingdom

JENNIFER REES LARCOMBE

KINGSWAY PUBLICATIONS
EASTBOURNE

ISBN 0 85476 913 7

Published by
KINGSWAY COMMUNICATIONS LTD
Lottbridge Drove, Eastbourne BN23 6NT, England.
Email: books@kingsway.co.uk

Book design and production for the publishers by
Bookprint Creative Services, P.O. Box 827, BN21 3YJ, England.
Printed in Great Britain.

To my mother,
the greatest storyteller I ever knew.

Contents

	Introduction	9
1.	More Dangerous than Dragons	13
2.	The Deadly Enemy	27
3.	Ruins and Ravens	51
4.	Paupers and Princes	65
5.	Cedric's Sword	77
6.	The Secret Room	85
7.	The Sweet-maker	97
8.	Giants and Dwarfs	107
9.	Castle Invincible	117
10.	The Guilty Secret	127
11.	The Sorry Tale of Baron Sebastian	145
12.	The Land of Disguises	155
13.	The Girl in the Cage	169
14.	Dungeons and Mice	179
15.	The Ugly Princess	189
16.	The Menacing Mountains	209

Introduction

This book has taken seventeen years to write because the stories have grown, like mushrooms, out of the darkness of some of my experiences during that time. The first story I wrote, 'Paupers and Princes', came to me while I was strapped in my wheelchair, in a Tunbridge Wells park. I had always been an achievement-orientated workaholic until serious illness struck, leaving me disabled and in constant pain. I felt I was a burden on my family and worth nothing any more, to God or man! Two years into the illness the Lord began to give me scriptures and insights, over several months, showing me that it was not what I did for him that mattered, it was my company he wanted most. I was sitting in the park wondering how to share that with other disabled people in a magazine article I had been asked to write. The fairy story I believe God gave me seemed to encapsulate everything he had been teaching me and, judging by their letters, the readers caught the meaning behind the story too!

It is not easy to bring up six children from a wheelchair,

and during those eight difficult years I was often attacked by depression, doubt and anxiety. It was while I was fighting these imps that the first story in this book, 'More Dangerous than Dragons', came to me so forcefully that I have retold it to myself many a time since, whenever a 'Morbid' jumps out to attack me.

In more recent years, since I received God's remarkable healing, I have faced situations that have been infinitely more painful than those eight years in a wheelchair! Yet God has continued to give me parables at significant points in my journey, and the insights they provide have given me the will to carry on. They always come when I am sitting quietly, alone in his presence, and are always accompanied by scriptures that deepen and explain the stories to me. Some, such as 'Ruins and Ravens' and 'The Secret Room', helped me profoundly while I was struggling to let go of the past in order to receive the inner healing and happiness that the Lord was offering me. Others, such as 'Dungeons and Mice' and 'The Girl in the Cage', helped me handle my lifelong problem with fear.

Being in full-time ministry, as a counsellor and itinerant speaker, has been tough and I've faced temptations and dangers. I believe 'The Sweet-maker' and 'Castle Invincible' were definite warnings, given when my ministry was becoming more important to me than God himself.

Over the years, God has given me parables for others as well. I often meet people who find it hard to understand God's forgiveness and his remarkable grace! The seed ideas for some of the Chronicles were definitely given to me as I prayed for them, and telling someone a story in a few simple sentences during a counselling session definitely brought understanding and spiritual insight.

My favourite Chronicle is the last in the book, 'The Menacing Mountains'. It came to me one day as I was praying about a talk I had to give in a London church. I needed to illustrate the agonising problem of unanswered prayer and the story went down so well 'on the night' that I have used it many times since. Recently I had an email from someone who heard me tell that story in Canada:

> Seven years ago I came to a conference where you gave five talks. I can't remember what they were about, or anything you said – except a story about a prince who climbed a mountain. It helped me through a major faith crisis I was facing at the time and I remember every single word of it to this very day.

How her message encouraged me! It is such an awesome responsibility to stand in front of people and try to explain how God thinks and feels about them in a way they will understand. I have used many of the parables in this book as illustrations for talks, while speaking to groups of all ages. So if you are a preacher too, you are more than welcome to try them – I know they work!

When Jesus wanted to explain a vital concept he often wrapped it in a story that people could enjoy and remember while they swallowed the 'pill' without effort. A parable is a story about human life that illustrates a spiritual truth, on the assumption that what is relevant in one sphere is relevant in the other. They cannot be taken literally; you just have to sift from the fiction the small nuggets of truth that speak to you personally rather than trying to see spiritual significance in every detail of the story. The same parable can also mean something different to each person who hears it, and can be understood at different levels according to the stage they have reached on their spiritual journey.

God speaks to us in many different ways, through Scripture, the example and experiences of others, human wisdom, music, dance, sculpture, paintings, drama, nature and by direct communication – his 'still small voice'. He also uses parables, however limited they may be. He made each of us so different, perhaps that is why he needs all these various methods of communication; he likes to find the one that is best for each individual!

So I offer you these stories with my love and prayers, but very tentatively because they are very much a part of me and my own private relationship with God. I realise they may not speak to you at all if you find it easier to hear God in other ways. If that is so, I hope you will enjoy them simply as stories, and I've tried to make that easier by linking them together with recurring characters and a main story line.

However, because the Chronicles came to me as part of my own devotional times, I hope others will use them like that too, either on their own or in a group – and perhaps even with a whole congregation. I pray that they will provoke thought, trigger discussion and lead to meditation on the Scriptures from which they arose.

Enjoy!

1

More Dangerous than Dragons

> Be self-controlled and alert. Your enemy the
> devil prowls around like a roaring lion looking
> for someone to devour. (1 Peter 5:8)

In the days of dragons and damsels in distress, when
knights wore armour and kings wore crowns even at
breakfast time, there lived a very rich and powerful ruler.
He was known throughout the world as Good King
Paxalom and he had such a vast and well-trained army that
he was the envy, and the dread, of all other kings.

'You could conquer the world if you wanted to,' his
friends would tell him, but King Paxalom loved peace so he
only went to war against greedy kings who attacked their
weaker neighbours.

Throughout his vast empire he was universally loved by
his subjects, but they were also a little afraid of him. He
had a way of knowing things about people that they did
not even know themselves, and it was rumoured that he
possessed the ancient recipe for a potion that could heal

any kind of sickness. Most people dismissed such ridiculous stories but they all agreed that their king was certainly the wisest man on earth.

One Monday morning the trumpeters on the castle battlements blew a deafening fanfare. Guards sprang to attention and the drawbridge was hastily lowered. The Knights of the Octagonal Table were riding in for a council meeting with their king. There was no greater honour that could be bestowed on a soldier than to be invested as a King's Knight; they were allowed to wear armour made of beaten silver, with purple ostrich plumes in their helmets. When one of them was killed in battle, which happened rather often, Paxalom chose another brave young warrior to take his place.

As they all filed into the council chamber that morning a new knight, Sir Roger, followed at the end of the line, his pristine armour squeaking obtrusively. The other knights shot him disapproving glances, muttering crossly about oil-cans, but he took no notice of them. This was the most glorious moment of his entire life. He had daydreamed about it since he was in nappies. Most of his boyhood had been spent fencing with his mother's broom, jousting at her washing as it hung on the line, or shooting arrows at her posterior as she bent to weed the garden. He had joined the army as soon as he could and his mother did not weep as she waved him goodbye!

His exploits in battle were soon famous and he had risen through the ranks at astonishing speed. And now his greatest moment had come and he wasn't going to let the other knights spoil it for him.

'I'll soon show them what I'm made of!' he thought, as

he sat down with a final screech from his armour.

'Don't sit yet!' they hissed with scowls of disapproval that would have shrivelled anyone . . . except Sir Roger. When they were all ready, standing to attention, their helmets under their arms, King Paxalom himself marched into the room. He was much taller than any of them, a giant of a man with piercing blue eyes that never missed a thing.

'Gentlemen,' he began, 'this morning we have the pleasure of welcoming a new knight to our assembly: Sir Roger the Bold.'

'Sir Roger the Bumptious!' muttered Sir Marmaduke, as they stowed their helmets under their chairs, and sat down.

The discussions that followed were long and boring but the new knight survived by imagining the day when the king would honour him with medals and garlands for some great military achievement. Sir Marmaduke was in the middle of a long speech when one of the king's famous carrier pigeons alighted on the windowsill.

'Oh dear,' said King Paxalom as he read the message attached to its claw. '*Oh dear!* This *is* bad news!' Sir Roger hoped fervently for a war that would display his daring but instead the king said, 'This letter is from my dear friend King Gustaff. All his ten children and many of the royal household have been struck down by a mysterious sickness. He implores me to send some of my healing elixir as quickly as possible.'

'Your Majesty's swiftest ships are in port!' said several knights at once.

'I'm afraid,' said King Paxalom heavily, 'there is no time to send the elixir by sea. Gustaff's family would be dead before a ship could reach them. I'll have to send someone by the short route, over land.' There was a horrified silence in the room; then the knights began to fidget or clear their throats nervously.

'Sire,' began the oldest, peering anxiously through his eyeglass. 'The short cut runs through . . . Forgive me, I hate to mention the name of the terrible place!'

'The Land of Utter Desolation,' finished Sir Marmaduke, who had no finer feelings. 'Sire, no one could possibly get through those dragon-infested forests.'

'We could *all* go, and take several regiments to protect us,' suggested another knight, without much enthusiasm. 'Safety in numbers, what?'

'No!' replied the king with a shudder. 'How could I risk the lives of so many brave men? And anyway, the chances of a whole troop getting through enemy lines would be nil; they would create far too much noise. No, our only chance is for one man to go alone. He might have a hope of slipping through unnoticed.'

'Yes but . . . which man?' asked several knights in unison, as they looked at each other apprehensively.

'I'll go, Majesty!' said Sir Roger. He was so eager he sprang to his feet, sending his chair crashing to the stone floor behind him. The other knights winced.

'Too dangerous!' said the king. 'You don't yet have enough experience. Those forest paths are guarded by some very cunning creatures.'

Sir Roger fell to his knees. 'Sire,' he pleaded, 'I implore you to let me go!'

'Why does he always have to be so theatrical?' whispered the other knights; but none of them offered to go instead. The king looked round at them all, then sighed heavily.

'It seems I have no choice,' he said reluctantly and hurried away to his secret dispensing room.

'At least the king has one knight who isn't afraid of a few dragons and giants!' said Sir Roger tactlessly.

'You don't know what you've let yourself in for, boy,' said Sir Marmaduke gloomily as the rest of the knights clanked away in search of ale.

When the king returned he was carrying a small glass bottle containing a thick, dark red liquid.

'Hide it under your breastplate,' he instructed. 'It would be a disaster if this elixir ever got into enemy hands, for it can cure all ills. Tell King Gustaff to give one drop to each patient, and they will recover instantly.'

'I'll guard it with my very life,' promised Sir Roger grandly. He was impatient to be on his way but the king still looked worried.

'People who go into those forests are often never seen again,' he said.

But Sir Roger only shrugged. 'I won't get lost. I'll navigate by the sun and stars,' he said, already backing towards the door.

'You won't if it rains,' replied the king acidly, 'and it always does in the Land of Utter Desolation. I've drawn you a map. Follow it carefully, and don't speak to anyone until you reach King Gustaff's castle.'

'You can trust me, Your Majesty!' Sir Roger said, as he hastily knelt to kiss the king's hand.

'But I'm still not sure if *you* trust *me*,' murmured Paxalom thoughtfully, 'and that's what really matters.'

The sun glinted on Sir Roger's polished armour as he

galloped out of the castle on his great white horse; ostrich plumes billowed from his helmet and his cloak streamed out behind him. For the first two days he rode hard, constantly peering through the forest trees for puffs of dragon smoke, and straining his ears for the rumble of giants' feet. At night he hardly let himself sleep but sat up beside his campfire poring over the king's map or reading a book on the art of dragon slaying. Long before first light he was up polishing his armour and sharpening his sword. However, the forest track seemed quite deserted and by the third day he was beginning to wonder why the king had been so worried. There were obviously no horrible monsters in these parts at all. Feeling rather disappointed he allowed his horse to slow down to a gentler pace. 'I wonder why His Majesty said it always rained here; the sun's lovely and warm today.' Sitting back in the saddle, he admired the scenery as he hummed his favourite tune.

Just at that very moment he heard a slight rustle in the undergrowth beside the path. Instantly he drew his sword and swung his horse round to face the enemy. But it wasn't a dragon that finally popped out from behind the brambles; it was just a little old man, no taller than a cat. He wore a grey coat and hat that matched his long hair and silky beard. Sir Roger opened his visor and mopped his forehead.

'Good day,' said the little man pleasantly. 'Mind if I keep you company for a while? It's lonely in these parts.'

'You're right there!' agreed Sir Roger. 'I haven't seen anyone for days.'

'People are too frightened to come here any more,' sighed the little man. 'We have to stay here, of course, to run the mines, but we have a terrible time dodging the dragons and giants.'

'You keep close to me,' said Sir Roger kindly. 'I'll look after you.' The little man smiled up at him so gratefully that the young knight felt mean letting him walk.

'Come on,' he said reaching down, 'my saddle's big enough for both of us.'

'You must feel hot in all that armour,' said the little man when he was settled. 'It's so muggy today.' Sir Roger hadn't stopped to think about it before, but had to admit he did feel uncomfortably sticky.

'Poor old you,' said the little man sympathetically. 'Who'd be a soldier?'

'How nice to find someone who understands,' sighed Sir Roger. 'Most people never stop to think how hard life is for us.'

'Poor old you,' repeated the little man, 'and I bet you're hungry too.'

'I am rather,' admitted Sir Roger, 'but I can't stop to eat. You see I'm on a very important mission.' The little man was such a good listener that Sir Roger found himself telling him everything.

'Fancy sending you out here all alone,' he said, looking shocked. 'Didn't any of the other knights offer to come with you?'

'They're a lazy lot!' Sir Roger snorted resentfully.

'Probably laugh at you behind your back too?'

'How ever did you know that?' gasped Sir Roger. No one else realised how miserable other people made life for him. 'They've got no right to treat me the way they do!' he thought, and suddenly he felt really angry. His new friend was just saying 'poor old you' once again when another little man jumped out from the undergrowth.

'Oh, here's my brother. Would you be able to give him a ride too?'

'Delighted!' said Sir Roger, and he meant it. These little people seemed so understanding – unlike a few knights he could mention!

'I hope you don't mind my saying this,' said the second little man with a polite cough, 'but are you *quite* sure you're on the right road to King Gustaff's kingdom?'

'Yes, of course,' frowned Sir Roger. 'My king gave me a map.'

'But suppose the map's not accurate?' queried the little man kindly.

'My king knows *everything*,' said Sir Roger. 'He'd never give me a faulty map.'

'Well, I'm sure he wouldn't *mean* to, but has he ever been here himself to check?'

'Well . . . no . . . but . . .'

The little man's brother patted Sir Roger's arm kindly as he added, 'It's ever so easy to *think* you're going the right way and then . . .' His voice trailed away in a shudder and left Sir Roger grappling with an icy feeling of doubt. What if this were the wrong way after all? Suppose the king was wrong? These little men lived here in these forests; surely they were bound to know best?

'Don't you worry,' they both said in chorus. 'We'll see you're all right. Oh, here are some of our cousins,' they added, as three more little men popped out from behind a boulder. They looked so small and tired that Sir Roger offered them a ride too, and soon one was sitting on each of his shoulders while the third squashed the plumes on his helmet. The horse snorted crossly but no one took any notice of him.

'What are you?' Sir Roger asked his new friends. 'Pixies or elves?' The little men looked most offended.

'We're Morbids,' they said. 'Haven't you ever heard of the Morbids?'

'No,' admitted Sir Roger blankly.

'We're faithful friends, we are,' whispered the Morbid on his left shoulder. 'We have a saying, "Give a Morbid a lift and he'll stick to you for life." Look! There's our poor old grandpa struggling along the path ahead of us. Do you think you could possibly let him sit between your horse's ears?' The horse rolled his eyes furiously at this suggestion but was too well trained to protest. The old grandpa sat facing Sir Roger and chatted away as if they had known each other for years.

'A knight on a dangerous mission needs a bit of company sometimes,' he said. 'Didn't your king realise how lonely you would be? He can't think much of you!'

'Oh, but he does!' said Sir Roger earnestly, but found himself wondering why the king had been mean enough to tell him not to talk to anyone on the journey.

'If you were worth more than an apple pip to him,' continued the old man, 'he'd have sent soldiers to protect you. Have you ever thought this could be a plot to get rid of you?'

Sir Roger knew the other knights didn't like him; suppose the king secretly felt the same? He was trying to sound much more cheerful than he felt as he said, 'Don't you worry about me, I'm perfectly safe. I haven't seen a single dragon so far.'

'Don't say that!' protested the Morbids with little gasps of horror. 'They're everywhere!' The little man on his right shoulder was shivering so violently he had to cling to Sir Roger's visor to stop himself falling.

'They'll be hiding up in those rocks, waiting, then suddenly they'll strike.' He was choking with terror by this time, and Sir Roger began to feel distinctly on edge too. He looked up anxiously at the craggy mountains that towered above the forest trees.

'I don't . . . er . . . see any smoke,' he said nervously.

'Well, you wouldn't,' quavered the frightened Morbids. 'They hold their breath when they're hiding, but surely you can feel all those pairs of evil red eyes watching you?' Sir Roger looked back over his shoulder. Come to think of it he *did* feel something. They were travelling through such a deep valley the sun seemed to have disappeared, leaving them surrounded by eerie shadows.

'This is just the kind of place dragons choose for an ambush,' whispered Grandpa as another group of Morbids hurried up to join them. 'Why not go back now, while you still have the chance?'

'I couldn't do that!' exclaimed Sir Roger, imagining the smug faces of the older knights, but he had to admit he was beginning to feel rather ill.

'Poor old you,' said the first Morbid kindly.

Soon there were so many Morbids that the horse had to wade through a surging grey sea of them. They swung from his mane and bridle until he began to stagger under their cumulative weight, and when two of them got between his hoofs, he fell, gashing his knees badly on the rocky path.

'Oh, the poor horse!' cooed the Morbids. 'He won't be able to walk for days.'

'But how shall I manage without him?' said Sir Roger frantically.

'Well, you can't leave him here,' said the Morbids in horror. 'He'd be dragon fodder before morning.'

'Don't worry,' said Grandpa. 'We'll hide him in our cave. We know all kinds of cures and remedies. We'll soon put him right. You can collect him on your way home.' Sir Roger felt terrible as he watched ten Morbids leading his limping charger away down a side path.

'Poor old you,' said the little voice beside him. 'No one will expect you to finish this mission without a horse!'

'He's right,' thought Sir Roger. 'The accident does give me an excellent excuse. But no,' he told himself with a martyr's sigh, 'my king needs me.'

'Look!' said Grandpa, pointing at the little footpath that branched off the main forest track. 'There's our short cut. It'll save you hours of time.'

'It's not shown on the king's map,' said Sir Roger doubtfully.

'Oh, he wouldn't know about it – it's far too small – but we'll show you the way.'

Sir Roger, feeling the Morbids were now his only hope, hurried after them thankfully.

On and on he climbed, surrounded by an ever-growing crowd of little grey men. They did their best to cheer him up, but their constant chatter was giving him a headache.

'You must be so tired,' they said, 'and that armour's so heavy. Why not let us carry it for you?' Thankfully Sir Roger unbuckled his breastplate and soon the kind little men were staggering along behind him carrying his helmet and shield on their shoulders. He was feeling so ill by this time he could hardly stand up, but nothing would persuade him to part with his sword.

They were trudging up a long hill when he stumbled over a particularly attentive Morbid and down he fell, banging his head hard on a rock.

'Poor old you,' he heard a little voice say through the swirling stars. 'It's all been too much for you.' He tried to stand up again but Morbids were sitting on his chest, wiping his face and patting the bump on his head.

'You need to stay here and have a good long rest,' said their soothing voices. 'You're a very sick young man. We'll take care of you.'

As Sir Roger drifted into a sleep full of nightmares he dreamed little fingers were feeling about inside his doublet, while tiny hands pulled his sword from its scabbard.

Suddenly he sat up, scattering little grey men in every direction. It wasn't a dream! It was happening!

He snatched back the precious bottle and, springing to his feet, he seized his sword from the troop of Morbids who were scurrying away with it.

'Get out of here, you disgusting little creatures!' he shouted, as he began to lunge, swipe and slash. 'You dismal, depressing, dishonest, deceiving, doubt-inducers! In the name of my king, get out!' The great sword whipped through the air, sending a shower of Morbid fragments in every direction, while those who were not chopped in half scuttled off into the forest, squealing with terror. Soon not one was left, and Sir Roger wiped the blade of his sword with his hankie and retrieved his map from a rabbit hole.

For once he felt too stunned to be pleased with himself.

Two days later a knight without armour or horse limped over the drawbridge of King Gustaff's castle.

'I am Sir Roger, Knight of King Paxalom's Octagonal Table,' he said, but the guards only laughed at him. Brave Sir Roger was almost in tears, when King Gustaff himself appeared. He took the bottle from the knight and shook his hand gratefully.

'Well done, lad!' he said. 'But I'm amazed you managed such a dangerous journey all alone.'

Sir Roger looked embarrassed. 'Actually, sire,' he admitted, 'I didn't meet any dragons or giants.'

King Gustaff looked puzzled. 'Dragons? Giants?' he frowned. 'There aren't any left these days! The enemies who haunt those forests are far more dangerous because most people never realise how deadly they are.'

2

The Deadly Enemy

Greater love has no one than this, that he lay
down his life for his friends. (John 15:13)

There was something that always intrigued Sir Roger, but
when he questioned the other knights as they quaffed their
ale they were always struck by a sudden attack of deafness.

'But I *must* know why King Paxalom has such remarkable powers,' he would shout as loudly as he dared, 'and
how did he discover that miraculous elixir?' When they still
did not seem to hear, Sir Roger would stomp away, muttering, 'One day I'll ask him myself!' And one day he did.

A terrible snowstorm had made the roads impassable
and none of the knights had managed to wade through the
drifts to reach the palace in time for their usual Monday
morning meeting around the Octagonal Table; that is
except for Sir Roger, who was more eager than the rest. All
the same, snow had got in through the joints of his armour
and by the time he was finally shown into the king's presence, he was so cold his teeth were chattering.

'Get rid of all that clanking metal, lad,' said King Paxalom, leading him into his private study. Soon Sir Roger's damp clothes were steaming nicely as he sat in an armchair by the burning logs, enjoying the mulled wine the king gave him. Perhaps it was this that lent him courage to ask his question at long last. Such a lengthy silence followed that Roger wondered if the king also had become deaf, or perhaps he had fallen asleep. But King Paxalom was not deaf or asleep; he was remembering.

The day it all began he had been sitting in this same chair, by the same fire in just such a snowstorm as this – but how different he had been! He could see himself as an enormous, gangling youth of eighteen, who had loved being a prince but did not want to be a king. How easy life had been while his grandfather was there to take the weight of the empire on his enormous shoulders, but the young Paxalom who sprawled by the fire that day was no longer a carefree prince. His grandfather had died three months before and with him had gone all his wisdom and strength. Suddenly a raw young man, little more than a schoolboy, was responsible for the welfare of millions of people, and the burden felt very heavy indeed.

That day, long ago, it had not been a curious young knight who had occupied the chair on the other side of the fire; his grandmother had sat there sewing, while her two massive hounds lay at her feet.

'You know, Grandmamma,' he had said suddenly, 'I wish I could change places with someone else. Anyone else in my kingdom would do – even a beggar!'

'Perhaps you should try it for a few days, dear,' she

answered dryly. 'Particularly in weather like this!'

At that moment the Lord Chamberlain hurried into the room looking extremely flustered.

'I am sorry to disturb Your Majesties,' he said, almost forgetting to bow, 'but we are facing a major national disaster! Messengers from Stenburgh have just brought terrible news!' Stenburgh was the largest city of the realm, lying sixty miles away at the far end of the great plain.

'They made that journey – in all this snow?' said the queen grandmother, astonished; and her dogs sprang to their feet, growling, as three men burst into the room with a lamentable lack of ceremony.

The Lord Chamberlain just had time to say, 'The messengers, Your Majesties,' before words began to explode from them like cannon balls.

'It's the Black Wizard! He's *come*! He's taken over the whole city and set himself up in your royal residence. He is rounding up everyone in the city who's good and honest, and having them killed in all kinds of horrible ways. Worse still, he is promoting men who are evil, greedy and cruel to positions of authority. We are doomed, Your Majesties! Dear knows how we managed to escape, for he's set his Dark Watchers at every gate of the city.'

'Who is this wizard?' asked Paxalom as he looked at the horrified faces of his grandmother and the Lord Chamberlain. 'I've never heard you mention him before.'

'No dear,' replied his grandmother. 'We felt it was wiser for you to enjoy your childhood. There was no point in worrying you before it was necessary, but he has always been your grandfather's most deadly enemy. He rules the Waste Lands far out on the edge of the world but he has long wanted our empire so he can call himself King of kings.'

'Typical of his cunning to choose this precise moment in time to make his move,' added the Lord Chamberlain bitterly. 'He knows Your Majesty is still young and inexperienced.'

'But we have the best army in the world,' protested Paxalom. 'Let's muster at once and drive this fellow out!'

'You are not playing with lead soldiers now, Paxalom,' said his grandmother reprovingly, and the Lord Chamberlain added heavily. 'Our armies would be useless against this wizard because he uses magic, not nice ordinary weapons like swords and javelins.'

'He has only been kept in check all these years,' added the old queen, 'by the strength of your grandfather's goodness and honesty.'

'Oh dear,' smiled Paxalom ruefully, as he remembered some of his more hair-raising childhood pranks; his grandmother was obviously remembering them too and she clicked her tongue in agreement.

'So what can we do?' asked the young king as a grey cloud of despair seemed to settle over the room.

After a long silence the Lord Chamberlain braced himself with an effort. 'Something must be done, and done very soon,' he said, 'or his power will spread throughout our whole empire and destroy us all. This evil creature will not stop until he has the entire world in his ugly grip.'

'So what can we do?' repeated Paxalom.

'We should sleep on it,' said the old queen firmly, and as she swept from the room she said, 'And Paxalom dear, don't read in bed!'

Paxalom wanted to say, 'I'm not a child,' but at that moment he felt as weak as a baby!

All night he lay, sleepless, in the great royal four-poster, his longing to change places with a beggar growing stronger by the minute. 'I can't handle a serious situation like this,' he muttered. He could hardly remember his father, who had died when he was only five, but knew exactly what his grandfather would have done. He would have ridden off through the snow in all his royal regalia, and told the wizard to go – and go fast! One word from his awesome grandsire had always been enough to quell the boldest rebel.

'But if I tried that,' thought Paxalom, 'the wizard would kill me and put my crown straight on his head! No, I need more information about him and how his magic works. I need a spy I can trust – someone who could get into Stenburgh, see what's going on and then come back to me with a plan of action. Yes! I need a spy disguised as a beggar, who could slip past those Dark Watchers at the city gates. But who can I possibly send on such a dangerous mission?'

Suddenly he sprang out of bed. 'I wanted to be a beggar,' he told himself. 'Now's my chance. I'll go to Stenburgh myself!'

The following evening a ragged, dirty figure joined a troop of serfs as they hauled sledges piled with firewood back into the city of Stenburgh. Paxalom had not told the Chamberlain or his grandmother what he intended to do because he knew they would stop him. Nor had he waited to give his plan any thought, because he was eighteen and waiting was not something he ever did. His two faithful pages, friends and accomplices since childhood, were the only ones who knew where he was when pandemonium hit the palace next morning.

'Don't tell them until I've been gone six hours!' he had ordered them firmly as they rubbed him with mud and greasy soot from the kitchen hearth. The rags were easily bought from one of the many beggars outside the palace gate, and it was not hard for one of the pages to take a horse from the royal stables and ride away unnoticed at such an early hour in the morning. No one saw the boy change places with a beggar waiting in the woods, and the noble animal galloped so fast through the mud and slush that it would have been impossible for anyone to recognise the king.

Now the exhausted stallion was safely stabled in a shed in the forest, while a delighted woodcutter told himself he must be dreaming as he gazed at the gold coin a 'beggar' had given him for his trouble.

The Black Wizard's men were on guard at the city gates and every stranger was stopped and questioned. Paxalom soon realised this as he cautiously approached the towering walls of Stenburgh; but it was then that he saw the serfs. He was sure he looked quite as dirty and bedraggled as they were so he slipped in among them. Because they thought he was one of the Black Wizard's spies, they were too afraid to do anything but ignore him. Once inside the city gates, they hurriedly shuffled off to their hovels, leaving him to sniff their waiting dinners and wonder how long it took to die of starvation. Paxalom had never gone a whole day without food in his life.

'Beggars beg,' he thought, 'so I'd better make a start.' A

few hours later he began to realise his grandmother had been right – she usually was! He had been turned away from innumerable doors, shouted at, pelted with rotten eggs, bitten by dogs, drenched with dirty water by irate housewives and beaten by their husbands. He was sore, wet, cold and very tired indeed.

At last he found himself in the main square of the city, which was dominated by his own royal residence. He stood looking up at the great windows from which he had so often waved at cheering crowds. He wondered, rather miserably, how many starving beggars had gazed up at him from this spot while he had been warm and well fed inside.

'If I ever get home I'll never let another beggar starve in my kingdom,' he vowed, and then hastily turned away, ashamed of the childish tears that stung his eyes.

A group of beggars were crouching in the snow near by. 'Get out of here!' one of them shouted rudely. 'You're not welcome on our patch.' They stood up threateningly, leaving Paxalom no option but to back away hastily. He felt dizzy with hunger, and the night was so bitterly cold he knew he would not survive without shelter.

'You hungry, youngster?' A little lame man, leaning on a stick, was looking up at him speculatively. 'You're a giant, you are!' he added. 'See that doorway? It leads into a bakery. The good wife's so tired tonight she wouldn't notice if you took a couple of loaves from her cooling rack.'

'I couldn't . . . t-t-take advantage of her,' stammered Paxalom. 'I've never stolen anything in my life, sir.'

'Maybe you've never had to,' growled the little man, eyeing Paxalom's well-developed physique, but the 'sir' had mollified him so he added, 'You have to steal to survive here.'

Suddenly terrible screams, angry shouts and pounding hoofs roused the drowsy city. A troop of horsemen with flaming torches galloped into the square. 'Wizard's men!' spat the cripple. 'They kill hundreds of us street people every night!'

By the time the soldiers had reined in their horses the beggars had all vanished, but kings of the royal blood are not used to running away, so Paxalom would have remained where he was, an easy prey for their swords, had he not been jerked backwards into a deep hole. The little lame man closed a trap door over their heads and consigned them both to darkness.

'Useful place this,' he remarked. 'Used to lead into a merchant's cellar but he bricked up the entrance and left this little cubby-hole. I wouldn't survive without it.' There was really only room for one small person and certainly not for a giant like Paxalom.

'Why does the Black Wizard want to kill innocent people?' he demanded, wishing his legs were not quite so long.

'He enjoys killing. He'll probably kill everyone in the city just to lure King Paxalom into attacking him.'

'But surely the king *ought* to come and get rid of this Black Wizard!'

The little man laughed bitterly. 'The king's only a child. No one can stop the Black Wizard – certainly not a useless wimp who's never even shaved.'

Paxalom wanted to protest that he had been shaving for a year, and if he were a wimp he would hardly be sitting here now, but he remembered he was a spy, just in time.

'How do you know so much?' he asked curiously.

'I don't,' replied the voice in the dark, 'but I've got a

friend who knows everything! He's a physician but some call him a saint. Lives on the far side of the city.'

'Does he *really* think there's no one who can stop this monster?' asked Paxalom.

'Well, the other day he did say that it would only be someone who was totally good who could stand up to such evil, and the wizard knows it! That's why he's killing off all the good people he can lay his claws on.'

'Is your friend good enough, do you think?' asked Paxalom hopefully.

'I wouldn't be surprised,' was the reply, 'but he won't get the chance. The wizard's onto him already; his time's running out.'

As they crawled from their hiding place in the grey light of dawn, stiff and aching, the little man said, 'By the way, people call me Small – I can't think why! What do they call you – Large?'

'That'll do fine!' laughed Paxalom.

'You aren't really a beggar, are you?' added Small suspiciously.

Paxalom did not reply. His grandfather had said that lying was something kings should never do.

'Running away from home I shouldn't wonder,' said Small caustically. 'Go back, lad. You won't survive here. I only took you in because you called me sir, but I won't again – you're too big.'

But there was a stubborn streak in Paxalom, or perhaps he was just very young, so he set off to walk the streets, hoping scraps of information would be easier to find than scraps of food. However, it was less than an hour before he was surrounded by soldiers and dragged, unceremoniously, through his own royal front door. He had seriously under-estimated the enemy's power.

The next minute he was standing before his grand-father's huge golden throne and feeling outraged to see it occupied by the Black Wizard himself. He was a tall thin man dressed, not surprisingly, in black. To Paxalom he looked more like a lizard than a wizard!

'I saw you from these windows last evening,' he said in a sharp, rasping voice. 'Who are you?'

Paxalom pointed to his ears and mouth and made a few gobbling noises in his throat.

'No! You're not deaf and dumb,' laughed the wizard. 'I saw the golden aura that surrounds you, so I had my men search for you all night. You are King Paxalom himself, I think – or another member of his accursed family – here to spy!'

Paxalom gobbled again, even more loudly, but a terrible blow from the soldier beside him sent him crashing to the marble floor.

'Take him to the torture chambers,' said the wizard with a yawn. 'Do your best but don't *quite* kill him. If he *is* Paxalom I want to stage a grand public execution to show the empire their precious king is dead. Then they're bound to surrender without resistance.'

The terrible things they did to Paxalom during the next six hours aged him twenty years. 'I wanted to do so much for my people,' he thought wretchedly, 'but now the only way I can help them is to keep quiet.' And he did – but at horren-dous cost. Finally, as he lay on the stone floor where the soldiers had flung him, he saw a pair of clawed feet hover-ing over him like a giant vulture preparing to drop on its prey.

'Well, Sergeant?' demanded the wizard's voice.

'Sir, I think this must be a brainless beggar and not the king,' replied the man apologetically. 'No youngster could possibly fail to confess after what we've put him through.' The sergeant had hardly finished speaking when there was a terrible sizzling sound and he melted to a pool of black stickiness which trickled slowly away through an iron grating.

'That is what I do to failures,' the wizard told the other cringing soldiers. 'Beggars don't have golden auras! Take him away and dispose of him. If he is King Paxalom everyone will soon realise he is dead, and if he is merely a royal spy the sooner he's exterminated the better.'

'What type of execution, sir?' asked a nervous voice.

'Beat him until every bone in his body is as soft as porridge,' snarled the wizard, and disappeared.

All the wizard's executions took place outside the city gate so the bodies could be forked easily into the mass graves that had been hastily dug there. As the men picked up their cruel clubs, Paxalom thought, 'No! I won't die and leave my people to such a tyrant as this,' but no one, however strong and determined, could possibly have survived those heavy blows. Death brought a swift release from pain. It was getting dark when the soldiers finally tipped his bleeding remains on top of all the other broken bodies and went home to have their supper.

When Paxalom opened his eyes he was lying in a room lit by one small candle. A man with a mop of red hair and a beard to match was peering down at him.

'You'll do!' he said with a satisfied grunt. 'You were dead

for at least two hours; you must be tough! No,' he added as
Paxalom eyed him wearily, 'I'm not one of the wizard's tor-
turers; I'm only an old physician. Your friend the little lame
man told me about a beggar who was well worth saving
and he showed me where you were. A farmer, who owes
me for the life of his baby, brought you here in his market
cart – covered with cabbages. One drop of my miracle-
working elixir was all you needed.' Paxalom did not
answer; he had fallen into a grateful sleep.

During the next few days he sat by the fire in the doctor's small room and watched him at work.

'Your heart will take longer to recover than your body,
lad, because my medicine works more slowly on hearts.'
He was right. All the wounds left by the torture and beat-
ing were merely scars, but his mind and emotions still felt
like wobbly jelly.

From dawn until late into the night the people came to
the doctor's door. The sick, sad, crippled and dying –
everyone was treated with respect and gentleness, and sent
away happier and better than when they arrived. As far as
Paxalom could see, this was the doctor's only reward, for
his patients were all far too poor to pay for the care he
gave.

'Sir,' asked Paxalom, as he and his host shared a meagre
supper of dry bread and boiled cabbage, 'you have treated
so many people today, but I have never once seen you give
them the miraculous medicine you used on me.'

'That can only be administered on very special occasions,' he replied sadly, 'because it is hard to make – and
extremely costly. The cures I use are mostly very ordinary,
the result of years of experience. But I do have one other

special gift to offer my patients . . .' He was about to say more, but a knock at the door interrupted him. By the time he had bandaged a wounded child, Paxalom was asleep again, on the hearthrug.

Early next morning they were both awakened by Small, who burst through the door without bothering to knock.

'Something's happening!' he began breathlessly. It seemed he had spent most of the night loitering around the barracks behind the royal residence. 'Just keeping my ears open,' was how he put it. 'The wizard's up to something!' he said, as the doctor made him sit down and Paxalom lit the fire. 'He's having a huge wooden platform built in the square, right in front of the palace. Some people say that's where he's going to execute King Paxalom, while others are sure he means to use it when he challenges the king to single combat!'

'That should be an interesting match to watch,' laughed the boy as he hung the kettle over the flames.

'No it wouldn't,' retorted Small gloomily. 'It would be over in two seconds and the wizard would rule the world. He's planning something nasty for today, I'm sure of it.' Looking up appealingly at the doctor he added, 'I came to plead with you to try and escape; the soldiers were being ordered to round up everyone who opposes the wizard before he puts on his mystery show.'

'Well, that definitely includes me,' laughed the doctor, 'but I shall not leave. You two should go.' Small and Paxalom both shook their heads and Small struggled to his feet.

'I'm going back to my post as I can't make you see sense,' said Small. 'I'm not sitting here doing nothing – not at a time like this!' Suddenly he had his arms round the doctor and was trying hard to blink away the tears. 'They'll be here for you soon,' he said sadly.

'So this is goodbye, is it, my friend?' asked the physician, holding him close. 'I have asked you many times before but, for the last time, will you let me heal that lame leg of yours with a drop of my elixir?' Small pulled himself firmly away from his old friend and the doctor sighed. Turning to Paxalom he said, 'I have wanted to heal him for so long but he won't have it. He tells me he's content to be a crippled beggar because he knows who he is, but if I made him straight and strong he fears he would lose himself. Even the most powerful elixir in the world cannot heal someone who is afraid to get well.'

Paxalom frowned. 'Well, I'm very glad he knows who he is and stays that way!' he said. 'If you had made him fit and strong he might not have bothered to befriend a fugitive beggar like me. I owe you my life twice over, Small, and I shall not forget it!'

The cripple and the king exchanged a smile of complete understanding, while the doctor shook his head at both of them.

When the door had been bolted behind him, the old man hurried Paxalom into his dispensing room. 'Quick,' he said, 'we obviously don't have long and there is something very important I need to do.'

The room was small and dark; shelves filled with rows of bottles lined the walls, and books were stacked up on the floor. They sat at the table while a single candle cast eerie shadows around them.

'When I was a young man,' began the doctor, 'a strange

being from another world appeared to me in this very room. He said he had been sent to give me a gift that I might not be willing to receive.'

'What was it?' asked Paxalom.

'A tiny seed, which he held out to me on the palm of his hand.'

'How did you know he was from another world?' Paxalom asked breathlessly.

'He glowed like a hot fire, and his clothes were the colour of flames,' replied the doctor. 'But I don't have time now to tell you more. He said the seed he held was the gift of love; if he planted it in my heart it would go on growing there all my life.'

'Why did he think you might not want such a beautiful gift?' enquired Paxalom.

'To love is costly!' replied the old man simply. 'It leaves you open to the agony of rejection. Real love is not a soft sympathetic emotion; it has to be hard sometimes – and is often misunderstood. As if that were not enough, love also feels the pain of others – and knows things about them that could be uncomfortable. No, love is not a pleasant gift to have! Hatred makes life on this earth much easier.'

'But you accepted it,' smiled Paxalom. 'I think it is love that heals your patients – as well as your medical skill.'

'They work together well,' nodded the doctor. 'I let him push the painful seed into my heart, and over the years it grew there until it finally broke my heart to pieces. Love does that sometimes; but it was then that I saw the Fiery One again and he told me how to make the elixir.'

'Has he been back since?' asked Paxalom, looking round the room apprehensively.

'Yes,' nodded the doctor. 'The night the Black Wizard swooped on the city. He said that my time here had come to an end. I must offer a seed of my love to someone I would be meeting very soon. This man would use it to win battles, bring peace to many and healing to more than I could ever hope to reach.' Standing stiffly to his feet, the doctor came round to stand beside Paxalom. 'I'm not quite sure who you are, boy, but you are definitely the one I have been expecting.'

'But I thought I needed wisdom more than love,' muttered Paxalom uncertainly.

'Love will bring wisdom, but wisdom without love is cold and dead. Do you want this seed, whatever it costs?'

'Yes, sir,' replied Paxalom. As the doctor pushed the tiny seed into his heart, the old man's forefinger felt more like the thrust of a sharp sword, which sent the boy rolling on the floor in agony.

Beads of sweat stood out on Paxalom's face as the old man helped him back into his chair, and while he gradually recovered his breath the doctor knelt down and began to pull up two of the paving stones. Underneath was a small hiding place, which contained a green glass bottle. Holding it in the candle's light he said, 'It's nearly full! That will never do.' And to Paxalom's dismay, he poured the precious liquid away.

'Why did you do that?' he demanded.

'Would you want the wizard's men seizing it for themselves?' he laughed. 'This elixir is so powerful that one drop on the tongue will cure any ill of body, mind or heart and ensure long years of strength and vigour. As you know, it can even raise the dead on rare occasions.'

'Yes, I can see it could be dangerous in the wrong hands,' said Paxalom ruefully, 'but how much pain it could ease!'

'Only if it were administered by someone who already had the gift of love,' said the doctor, 'and that is why I am giving it to you.'

'But you just poured it all away!' The doctor reached back into the hiding place and produced a small lead casket, inside which was folded a piece of parchment. He handed it to Paxalom with a chuckle.

'Here is the recipe, but I'm afraid you won't be able to understand it. I've never met a beggar who could read Greek.'

Paxalom was smiling as he smoothed the parchment out on the table, but by the time he had finished reading the faded characters, his eyes had widened in consternation.

'Surely there must be an easier way to make it than this,' he faltered. 'Does it *really* have to be a mixture of my own blood, sweat and tears?'

'Yes, boy, I'm afraid so. And the blood can only come from wounds inflicted on you unfairly; the sweat from unpaid work done to benefit others, and you must shed the tears for someone else's pain. The finest healers are those who have suffered themselves.'

'But sir,' laughed Paxalom, 'while I am busy crying, bleeding and sweating, how am I supposed to collect the ingredients?'

'You won't have to. After you have suffered with or for someone else, you will find the drops have been gathered for you and carefully bottled and corked.'

They were both becoming aware of a commotion

outside in the road. Horses' hooves were approaching, and the tramp of heavy boots; people screamed, doors banged, dogs barked. Hastily the doctor folded the parchment and pushed it back into the casket; then, pulling a leather bag from a drawer, he put both bottles inside.

'Take it!' he ordered briskly, as he pushed Paxalom towards the ladder that led to the loft above. 'Hide up there until they've taken me.'

'Give me a knife or even a poker,' demanded Paxalom, 'so I can defend you.'

'Foolish boy,' smiled the doctor. 'They would only take you too, and the elixir would be lost for ever.'

As Paxalom reluctantly clambered up the ladder, they could already hear the wooden planks of the door splitting under heavy axe blows. The doctor reached up and grabbed one of Paxalom's long legs. 'If you are who I think you are,' he said softly, 'remember the tears, blood and sweat of a suffering king goes a thousand times further than that of an ordinary man like me. Go now!' And with that he turned to meet his fate.

Several hours later Paxalom crawled out of the loft with the leather bag tied round his waist. He felt sick when he thought of what the wizard's men would probably be doing to his friend.

'I want to go home!' he thought miserably. Everything in him longed to find some way of slipping through the city gates, dashing to the forest to find his waiting horse, and riding all night to the safety of his grandmother's fireside. Yet as he looked into the worn, frightened faces of the people he passed, something told him he had to stay. He did not realise it was the seed of love taking root in his heart.

Suddenly the sound of shouts and trumpet blasts brought the city smartly to attention. Soon everyone seemed to be hurrying towards the main square, while impatient soldiers prodded them along with their lances.

'Don't keep the wizard waiting,' they shouted. 'He's about to make a speech.'

'Oh no,' thought Paxalom. 'If I get anywhere near him, he'll see that dratted aura he says I've got.' But there was no escaping those wicked prongs. It seemed obvious that the wizard would use the wooden platform that now jutted from the front of the palace, so Paxalom guessed the further he kept away from it the better. 'If I could only find Small's hole I'd be safe,' he thought, edging towards that corner of the square. But so many people had been herded into the area that he could hardly move. Suddenly a roll of drums silenced the crowd and the wizard himself stepped onto the platform.

'Hail, O Great One,' shouted the obedient people, but Paxalom distinctly heard someone say, 'Don't look at him, boy.' Looking down instead, he saw Small peering anxiously up at him. 'He wants to enslave their minds; that's what my poor old friend said he would try next. So don't listen, boy, or you'll be doomed to serve him like the rest of them.'

Paxalom slithered down inside the solid wall of people until he crouched at Small's level. They were pleased to see each other, in spite of the solemnity of the occasion.

'They did for him an hour ago,' said the little cripple as more tears disturbed the grimy coating of his face. 'What's left of him is in that awful pit now. Why couldn't he have saved himself?' He stopped abruptly because the crowds were silent; the wizard was speaking.

'Your lives are about to begin. No longer will you be downtrodden and abused by a tyrant king, forced to work and starved to death. I am your saviour! I promise you wealth, comfort and freedom!'

'Oh yes?' muttered Small. 'He's the biggest liar who ever lived!' When the wizard stopped suddenly, in mid-sentence, the little man scrambled onto Paxalom's shoulders to see what had interrupted his flow. 'Trouble!' he remarked, slithering down again. 'Keep your head down, boy.'

'I have just had a report from one of my Dark Watchers,' continued the wizard's voice ominously, 'that King Paxalom himself has been seen in the city, right here among us! Spying! Seeking a way of enslaving you all again.' A murmur ran through the crowd and everyone began to look about expectantly. 'Hiding like the young coward that he is!' continued the wizard. 'Let him come forth and face me like a man.'

'I've done that once already,' thought Paxalom, ducking lower still, but the wizard's next words froze him.

'I challenge you, King Paxalom, to single combat. If you win I will leave your empire for ever. If I win you die and I rule.' There was a long, suffocating silence in the square; no one moved, they hardly dared to breathe. When he spoke again the wizard's voice sounded soft, almost wheedling.

'I am a frail old man, but you are a strong young soldier. You have been trained to wield a sword. Don't be afraid.'

'Liar!' hissed Small. 'His evil magic is more powerful

than any sword.' Another long silence followed.

'I know you are near, I can sense you!' The wizard sounded angry now. 'I am about to order my soldiers to move through this crowd, killing your subjects one by one until there are none left in this square! You have three minutes to decide whether to come forward voluntarily or wait until we find you.' A terrible shiver went through the helpless crowd as they stood penned in by the soldiers. Somewhere a woman began to wail.

'How far are we from your cubby hole?' asked Paxalom urgently.

'It's right behind you,' whispered Small, 'but there must be at least four people stood on the trap door.'

'As soon as they move I want you to hide something in there for me,' said Paxalom, 'something your friend gave me, which no one else must *ever* have.'

'He trusted his medicine to *you*!' whispered Small incredulously.

'Only the recipe,' admitted Paxalom, 'but I need you to look after it for a while. And if I never come back – burn it.'

'Just who are you?' demanded the cripple.

'Your king,' replied Paxalom quietly, 'so you owe me your unquestioning obedience.' And he hung the leather bag round Small's neck.

'You won't win against him.' There were more tears on the wrinkled face now.

'Perhaps not,' replied Paxalom grimly, 'but I can't stay here and watch my people being slaughtered while I have the chance to save them.' Before his friend could answer he was elbowing his way to the front of the crowd.

The soldiers who surrounded the wooden platform barred his way but the wizard recognised him at once. 'I thought I had already killed you,' he snarled savagely.

Paxalom charged up the steps to stand face to face with his terrible enemy. He had been shivering with fear just a moment before, but suddenly he was so angry with this monster whose greed had cost so much suffering that his ferocious glare was worthy of his grandfather.

'I have no sword with which to fight you,' said Paxalom, 'but I guess a sword would be useless against your weapons. So I merely ask that you will take my life and let these people go free.'

The wizard gasped and fell backwards, as if a violent blow in the chest had winded him. When his minions pulled him to his feet he looked frightened and shrank away from Paxalom like a whipped dog. 'Such accursed goodness,' he whimpered. 'I never guessed, I didn't realise.'

Suddenly Paxalom remembered Small's words: 'Only someone who is totally good could stand up to such evil.' 'Well,' he thought, 'I'm sure I'm not totally good, but I know what my grandfather would do right now.' Pointing an accusing finger at the wizard he thundered, 'Get out of this empire, you evil lizard – you have no right here! You are defeated!'

Again the wizard fell backwards. Then, with a terrible cry, he leapt into the air surrounded by a cloud of his evil attendants. Like a great flock of bats they flew away towards the distant mountains.

Then the cheering began. Shouts of 'Long live King Paxalom!' were echoed by cries of joy from further away. 'The king's army has stormed the city gates! The Octagonal

Knights are riding into Stenburgh!'

Into the square rode the old queen herself at the head of the army and, while the ecstatic crowds roared their welcome, Paxalom hurried down the steps to help his grandmother dismount.

'You look rather dirty, dear,' was all she said.

Before he could answer, someone tugged urgently at his ragged coat. 'This might come in useful one day,' said a little lame beggar, handing him a leather bag. Before Paxalom could answer he had disappeared into the crowd. However many times the king searched the city streets, he never saw Small again.

Sir Roger's discreet cough startled the king, and with difficulty he roused himself from his memories.

'Ah, yes,' he said. 'You were asking how I came by the elixir. Oh, it's not much of a story really. Someone I happened to meet gave it to me – years ago. Have some more wine, Sir Roger? And tell me about that horse of yours.'

3

Ruins and Ravens

Forget the former things; do not dwell on the past. See, I am doing a new thing! Now it springs up; do you not perceive it? I am making a way in the desert and streams in the wasteland. (Isaiah 43:18–19)

When Good King Paxalom had worn his grandfather's crown for twelve years, and had won so many battles that everyone said it fitted him very well, he met a young woman who had been sad all her life. She lived in a tumbledown hovel at the edge of the woods, not far from the palace. Her father had been one of the royal dishwashers, but he turned all his pay into drink and left his daughter to beg or starve. He beat her regularly whenever he was drunk, and never bothered to mend the roof, even though it leaked like a sieve. Finally, in order to pay a debt, he promised her in marriage to a worse drunkard than he was and died in his cups the day before the wedding. Sophia's new husband was worse than her father and beat her even more.

One crisp autumn day she took her basket and went off into the woods to hunt for blackberries and cobnuts, for there was nothing to eat in her larder. The sun shone through the leaves so delightfully that she walked far deeper into the woods than ever before. She knew it was full of monsters, trolls and goblins, but they seemed far less frightening than the human beings in her life.

In a clearing she discovered a pool surrounded by reeds. The water was so still and clear she saw her own reflection for the first time in her life. Instead of realising how beautiful she was she merely wished her eyes were blue instead of green and her straight black hair had been blonde and curly.

'You're so ugly!' she told the girl in the pool, as she tried to rub away the bruise her new husband's fist had left on her cheek.

'I don't think you're ugly.' Startled, she sprang gracefully to her feet, scattering nuts and berries in all directions. She had been so engrossed in hating herself she had not realised she was being watched by a tall man in hunting clothes.

'Your Majesty!' she gasped, making him a deep curtsy. Because he said nothing, she curtsied again, then slowly her large green eyes dared to look up into his face, and for a long time they stood gazing at each other.

'Where . . . where do you live?' the king asked at last.

'By the wood, near your palace, Majesty,' she replied, curtsying for the third time.

'Why do you look so sad?' he asked gently, as he looked at her bruised cheek.

'Sire, I've always been sad,' she replied. 'I'm not sure I'd know how to feel happy, even if I were.' A delightful blush spread across her cheeks as she added, 'You must think me very vain, sire, looking at myself for so long, but I've never seen my own face before today.'

'You seemed disappointed,' smiled Paxalom.

'I don't like green eyes, sire.'

'But I do,' murmured the king softly and bent to help her gather the scattered contents of her basket. It was then that he noticed the plain brass wedding ring on her finger.

'I'm sorry, mistress,' he said stiffly. 'I must bid you good day.' And with a bow he walked quickly to the edge of the clearing where he had tethered his horse.

For a long time after he had ridden away, Sophia stood gazing after him, knowing she would never be the same again.

Dusk was falling before she found the familiar path that led to her home, but she was uneasy. Something was wrong: the sun ought to be sinking in the west, but the northern sky was crimson instead. As the trees began to thin she realised it was not the sunset she could see – it was her blazing cottage. Her husband, drunk and snoring by the hearth, had not heeded the log that slipped onto the shabby rug, and while he slept the cottage burnt down around him.

When Sophia finally ran out of the wood, her neighbours shook their heads sadly. 'Good riddance,' they told her. 'You're better off without a man like him.'

'But I've lost my home,' she sobbed. 'I was born here. Wherever shall I live now?'

Next morning the blackened ruin looked more desolate than ever as she stood forlorn by the garden gate. Perhaps she could go to the palace and ask if they had any room for a new housemaid?

A rider emerged from the trees, but she was too miserable to look up and see who he was. Even when he dismounted and came to stand beside her, she did not move, assuming it was the bailiff come to evict her.

'This was your home?' She recognised the voice at once. 'Was it your husband who died in the fire?' She bowed her head and curtsied as he asked gently, 'Where will you go now?'

'Oh, Your Majesty,' she whispered, 'I was wondering if you had any need of a housemaid. I'm good at cleaning and cheap to keep; I don't eat much.'

The king knew it took a multitude of housemaids to run his huge palace, but he did not want her as a servant. One glance from her big green eyes had won his heart for ever.

'Sire,' she pleaded, 'I've nowhere else to go.'

'Let me take you home to my grandmother,' he said at last. 'Perhaps she and I together can teach you how to be happy.'

King Paxalom's grandmother was still an imposing woman, in spite of her ninety years – almost as tall as her grandson, and straight as a lance. Her silky white hair was so long it reached the ground, and she wore it in two tight plaits, which she used to administer sharp slaps when anyone was unfortunate enough to displease her. Behind her forbidding frown (and painful plaits) she had a heart as soft as honey – and she loved Sophia on sight.

'Yes, dear,' she said to her grandson, when she had settled the exhausted girl in a four-poster bed, 'she'll do for you perfectly. Well, that *was* why you brought her to me, wasn't it?'

They were married a month later. King Paxalom's people were slightly surprised that he had not married some mysterious foreign princess, but once they had seen Sophia smile they had to agree that he could not have found a more beautiful queen anywhere in the world.

But not everyone lives happily ever after, not even in a fairy tale.

A few months after the wedding the young king climbed the spiral staircase to his grandmother's apartments and, sitting awkwardly on the edge of his stool, he began to talk about the weather. When he asked her for the fourth time how her rheumatics were that day his grandmother slapped him hard with both plaits.

'Come to the point,' she said. 'Something is bothering you.'

'I don't think Sophia is happy,' said King Paxalom miserably. 'I've tried everything. I've given her presents, planned balls, hired jesters – and she always smiles and says "thank you," but . . . but . . . I can feel the sadness in her. I can't seem to take it away. She keeps a part of herself locked away from me and no amount of knocking on that invisible door will make her let me in.'

'Poor Sophia,' murmured the old lady with unusual tenderness. 'Happiness is an art that has to be learned.'

'Then why can't I teach her?' demanded Paxalom. 'I'm not even sure she loves me,' he said, as tears stung his eyes. 'Isn't it ironic?' he added. 'I'm so rich and powerful I can have practically anything in the world I want, except the one thing I want most – Sophia's love and happiness!'

'You work too hard!' snapped his grandmother. 'Spend less time in your study and more with your wife.'

'Grandmamma, I often walk away from boring ambassadors and endless meetings so we can sit by the fire together or walk in the gardens, but I can never find her. I ask her ladies-in-waiting where she is and they tell me she's gone out. I don't have to ask them where – I *know!* She puts on that terrible old black shawl she was wearing the day I brought her to you and she goes back to weep in the ruins of her cottage. Grandmamma, why does she keep hanging round that awful place? Should I give orders for it to be flattened and the stones carted away?'

'Good gracious no!' snapped the old queen, impatiently slapping him again. 'One day she may ask you to do that, but it's her decision, not yours. Give her time.'

But time went by and the invisible wall dividing them grew higher and thicker all the time. Few people were aware of it; most saw a young queen who seemed born to the position. She worked hard doing all the good things queens do; she wore the right clothes and made the right remarks and smiled sweetly all the time. Only the most observant saw the sorrow in her beautiful green eyes.

One morning in spring, Queen Sophia woke to find the sun streaming through her open windows. It was still a shock to find herself in a soft feather bed and to sit up without feeling sore and stiff from kicks and blows. Paxalom was never angry with her, although she always expected him to be – tenderness was so new to her.

Paxalom always rose at five to work in his study until

breakfast: there was only a dent in the bolster beside her where he had been.

'If only I could show him how much I love him,' she whispered sadly. 'Why can't I be happy? He has given me everything I could ever want, but there's something black in my heart which keeps pushing love and happiness away.'

It was time to ring for her ladies-in-waiting to come and begin the royal ablutions and then the dressing and coiffeuring ceremonies. They would take at least two hours, but she loved it. She liked her ladies, adored the clothes and jewels the king had given her and, now that she was well fed, even she had to admit she was beautiful; but there on the sill, eyeing her through the open window, stood the ravens – waiting; watching; demanding.

'I'll come and feed you,' she told them nervously. 'I promise I'll be there after breakfast. Why can't they leave me alone?' she thought wretchedly. 'They're destroying my chance of happiness.'

The king and queen sat at breakfast, either end of the great oak refectory table, silent, both in their separate, isolated bubbles.

'I have to go through piles of dull papers this morning,' said the king at last. 'It would mean so much to me if you would sit with me – perhaps you could bring your sewing.' He knew she would say no. She always went to her old cottage after breakfast, but still he hoped.

'I have too much to do today,' she replied awkwardly and flushed as she saw the pain in his eyes. Inwardly she longed to run the length of that table and abandon herself to his love, while she told him about the horrible ravens. Instead, she rose stiffly from the table, curtsied formally and went her way. Paxalom sighed, returned to his study and locked the door.

Sophia hurried back to her apartments, pulled her black shawl from a chest and went down her private stairway to the garden. As she ran down the path she did not notice the flowers and frothy pink blossom. To her, everything seemed covered in a grey cloud of despair.

As she reached the ruins of her cottage she pulled the shawl around her like a shroud and began her morning ritual. She felt compelled to walk through the fallen stone walls and stand in the ruins of each little room, remembering. Her memories were not pleasant, most were painful and shaming – yet she still had to relive each one. She finished by walking round the overgrown garden and then stopped to lean on the gate, gazing at every detail, while the tears ran down her cheeks. In the woods nearby, the bluebells were at their best, but she never noticed them.

'Why must the past control me like this?' she thought as she looked up at the ravens. They were both there, as usual, perched on top of the blackened chimney looking down at her, waiting.

'My father and my husband,' she whispered. Why couldn't she be free of them? She took bread from her pocket and crumbled it on the ground at her feet. Down they swooped, gobbling it greedily and then, cocking their heads, they mocked her with evil black eyes. Sophia was sure that in those birds resided the essence of all that her father and husband had been. 'I hate you,' she muttered. 'You're ruining my life!'

Just then the crunch of footsteps behind her startled the birds and, with harsh squawks, they flew back to their perch. Coming towards her, along the path from the palace, was a large armchair carried on poles by four muscular footmen. Sitting in it, rigidly upright, was the queen grandmother. She only went out on momentous occasions, so Sophia watched her approach apprehensively.

'Put me down,' ordered the dowager, using both her plaits like riding crops to administer a rain of slaps on the heads of her sweating henchmen, 'and then go away.'

Sophia curtsied, embarrassed at being discovered here, and wishing she had hidden her shawl. She knew it must look strange, covering her exquisite gown.

'This, I take it, is where you used to live.' Sophia blushed and curtsied again. 'You must have loved it very much.'

'Oh no, madam!' replied Sophia so abruptly she almost sounded rude. 'I hate the place.'

'Then why do you come back here every day? I see you from my window.'

'Something pulls me back,' mumbled Sophia miserably. 'I can't stop it.'

'Well, you're going to have to decide who you want to be,' said the old lady. 'Queen or pauper? You can't go on being both!'

'Of course, I want to be Paxalom's wife. I want to love him and make him happy, but there is something in my heart that ties me to the past and won't let me accept this new life.'

'It's hatred,' said the old lady quietly. 'That is what fills your heart, child.' Sophia looked up, astonished. 'Oh yes,' the queen grandmother smiled, 'I know how sweet natured you are – I love you for it – but when anger is not allowed to be expressed it gets stuck inside the heart and eventually turns to hate.'

'But madam,' protested poor Sophia, 'I have never dared to be angry in my life.'

'Quite so!' said the dowager, waving a triumphant finger. 'When the little girl who lived in this cottage was beaten and starved, she swallowed her feelings because she could not let them show. When the bride was kicked and punched, naturally she was angry, but dared not let it out. Your heart is so full of hate now there is no room left in it for love or happiness.'

'How can I get rid of it?' sobbed Sophia. 'Please tell me, madam!'

With one knotted finger the old lady pointed up at the ravens on the chimney and the girl beside her knew exactly what she meant. 'They control all I do and say,' she whispered. The relief of being able to put her fears into words was enormous, but the old lady was shaking her head.

'No, they don't control you,' she said. 'They are only black memories from your past. And memories can only control you if you allow them to do so by coming here and feeding them every day.'

'But they *make* me,' said Sophia.

'No, it's the way you feel about your father and first husband that is destroying you – and Paxalom as well. There comes a time when we have to forgive those who have hurt us in the past; let go of them; set them free. While you continue to hold onto your grudges you bind yourself to them and give them power to hurt you.'

'Forgive them!' snorted Sophia indignantly. 'Madam, you have no idea what they used to do to me!'

'Perhaps not!' replied the old lady crossly. 'But it isn't me we're discussing. It's *your* choice. You have a perfect right to be miserable if you prefer to be.'

A cuckoo mocked Sophia from the woods, and a careless woodpecker drummed for its dinner; the silence between the two queens lengthened, while the older lady deftly swatted flies with her snow-white plaits.

'How *do* you forgive?' asked Sophia at last.

'With great difficulty,' snapped the old lady. 'It usually takes a lifetime, but it's deciding to start that counts. Tell those ravens to go. Tell them you'll never feed them again. Order them to leave and not to stop flying until they reach the Land of Utter Desolation. That's where they belong, so tell them to stay there, permanently.'

'But they won't do what I say,' said Sophia. 'They never have.'

'Oh yes they will, because of who you are! Of course they wouldn't obey the helpless little peasant girl who was in their power, but you have married the king! He rules our empire, so all his authority is yours, simply because he chose to make you his queen. Use that authority – now.'

Slowly Sophia turned towards the birds. The two black shapes hunched on the charred ruins of the cottage chimney stood out in sinister contrast to the sky above.

'Go . . . go away,' she said tentatively. They squawked derisively but they did not move. Rage, born of despair, suddenly seized her. 'Be off with you *at once*,' she ordered, stamping her foot, 'or my husband will be after you!' To her astonishment both birds flew away instantly, croaking with fear.

'If only I'd realised it was as easy as that,' she murmured, 'I'd have done it months ago.'

'Now tell me why you keep wearing that awful old shroud,' continued the queen relentlessly.

'It isn't an awful old shroud!' protested the girl sharply. 'It comforted me and kept me warm through so many cold winters. I feel safe when I'm inside it.'

'Becoming a new person means being willing to throw away the things that were important in the old life, however comforting they were,' snapped the dowager. Sophia said nothing for so long the old lady slapped her hard.

'You enjoy being unhappy, you do!' she snorted. 'You wear misery like you wear that cloak!'

'Oh madam,' cried Sophia, bursting into tears, 'is there no hope for me?'

'Of course there is, stupid child! Take that shroud off and burn it. I've brought my tinderbox. Gather some dry twigs – and hurry up, it's time for my nap.'

The fire burned well and the shawl was soon reduced to ashes.

'Good!' said the dowager. 'Now you can't cover up your lovely new clothes any more. Wear them with grace, child. Paxalom gave them to you because he loves you.'

They both smelt of smoke when the king arrived, followed by the four nervous footmen.

'Take me home at once,' ordered the old lady. 'I'm exhausted.'

When the chair and its crusty occupant had safely disappeared through the iron gates of the palace garden, Sophia left her bonfire and shyly approached the king. She was in his arms before she could say a word, sobbing with relief and joy.

'I wish we could destroy this place where I was so

unhappy,' she said very much later as they walked back, hand in hand.

'But surely a blank patch of ground would make you sad every time you passed it,' said Paxalom.

'Could we extend the palace garden walls and enclose my little strip?' she asked. 'We could make it into such a lovely private corner, just for ourselves. We could sit together in the evenings and listen to the birds in the wood while we watched our children play.'

Paxalom smiled down at her. 'You mean turn something sad and ugly into a place of peace and beauty?' he said thoughtfully. 'Yes, I like that idea.' And lifting her into his arms, he carried her home.

4

Paupers and Princes

> He came to that which was his own, but his own did not receive him. Yet to all who received him, to those who believed in his name, he gave the right to become children of God. (John 1:11–12)

There was nothing King Paxalom loved more, at the end of a long hot day, than to play with his children in their private corner of the palace garden. Here the stately monarch, who held the power of life and death over millions, could roll around on the grass being a horse for a small prince or a toy mender for a tiny princess.

'We are so lucky to have children,' he said to Queen Sophia, as they sat there together in the cool of the evening. 'My great great grandfather had none, and it was such a grief to him.' Sophia could see by the dreamy look in his eyes that Paxalom was about to launch into one of his stories. Smiling, she put down her sewing and pulled her sleepy daughter onto her knee. The heir to the throne abandoned the brick castle he was building and curled up at his father's feet.

'Yes,' began the king, 'the poor man was so lonely. No one ever believes a king could be lonely surrounded by so many courtiers and visiting royalty, but my great great grandfather definitely was. No number of bowing officials and scurrying servants could ever make up for having no children of his own. Whenever he rode down the hill to the city and through the streets in his golden coach, the very sight of a child would bring tears to his eyes.'

'Sir,' interrupted the prince, who was just old enough to understand about such things, 'why didn't he get married?'

'Ah,' replied his father, 'he *was* married, but the queen flatly refused to have children. "I'm not having all those sticky fingermarks and muddy footprints in my nice clean palace!" she would say. Everything had to be perfectly clean before she was happy. She made the royal maids scrub the marble floors *twice* every day, as well as polishing the gilded furniture and silver door knobs. Sometimes my poor great great grandfather used to stand at the palace windows looking longingly towards the city, thinking of all the children who lived there. "I have so much love to give," he would say sadly, "if only . . ."'

Then one day a terrible thing happened. The queen was making her daily cleanliness inspection up in the palace attics when she saw a spider's web! The whole court was instantly in uproar! Several maids were banished to the dungeons in disgrace, doctors hurried to help the hysterical queen and a very long ladder was hastily carried up the stairs.

'There is only one person in the world I can trust to remove this terrible disgrace,' said the queen, 'and that person is *me*.' With that she climbed the ladder, armed with a duster. Just as she reached the top, and began swiping vigorously at the terrified spider, she overbalanced and fell head first – and that was the end of her!

A huge sigh of relief rippled round the palace and the maids threw a party in the servants' hall that night. The following day the king called an emergency meeting round the Octagonal Table.

'Gentlemen,' he said, 'as soon as the funeral is over I intend to have children. Hundreds of them.'

'Has Your Majesty anyone particular in mind for the royal bride?' asked the startled Lord Chamberlain.

'Oh, there isn't time at my age to do it that way!' snapped the king. 'I want ready-made children – and I want them at once. Have all the spare bedrooms redecorated – nursery rhyme curtains, that kind of thing. Contact toy-makers all over my kingdom and have toys brought here to the palace. Order dressmakers to run up clothes for every size and shape of child, male and female. Engage nannies, tutors and governesses – but only the nice sort – and tell the cooks to organise the biggest children's party of all time. There could be as many as a thousand,' he added, his eyes gleaming. 'Get all that done by this time next week.'

'But sire,' spluttered the Lord Chamberlain, 'where are all these children coming from?'

'Didn't I tell you that?' said the king absently. 'I'm going down to the city to collect all the street children who have no homes, parents, food, clothes and certainly no love. I'm going to invite them to come up here and live with me in the palace. I will be their father and they will be my princes and princesses and will inherit my kingdom. So I must teach them how to be good and loving rulers for my people.'

The Lord Chamberlain was making a strange gurgling noise in his throat, so his assistant asked tentatively, 'But Your Majesty, if you take on so many children at once, surely you won't be able to love each of them individually?'

'Oh yes I shall!' said the king. 'I've got so much love to give.'

So the day after the queen's funeral the king set off for the city in his gold coach, wearing his best red velvet robes, trimmed with ermine, and his second best crown. He had worn his best crown the previous day and the weight of it had seriously squashed his ears.

When he arrived in the main square of the city he sent his guards to round up all the street children, and soon they were all standing in neat but nervous rows on the cobblestones.

'There really *are* thousands of them!' said the Lord Chamberlain, mopping his forehead. For a moment he almost wished the queen were back, but the moment passed rapidly.

The worthy citizens looked on smugly. 'At long last the king's going to do something about this plague of thieves and beggars we've had to suffer for so long,' they told each other. 'I wonder if he'll have them drowned like unwanted puppies or use them as slave labour in his coal mines.'

The royal trumpeters stepped forward and blew a

piercing fanfare, and the town crier yelled, 'Oyez! Oyez! Pray silence for His Majesty!'

The king opened his mouth to speak, but as he looked at the rows of thin, ragged waifs, tears began to trickle down his cheeks and his long and carefully written speech was forgotten. *How* he loved them!

'Will you come with me and let me be the kind of father you never had? Come and be my companions and the joy of my heart.'

The good citizens and the street children alike were stunned into horrified silence. As the silence lengthened the king blew his nose several times, very loudly, and the Lord Chamberlain tapped his foot nervously.

Then the whispers began running up and down the lines of dirty children.

'Must be a catch somewhere!'

'Too good to be true!'

'Sure to be strings attached!'

'If we go up there and live in the palace, we'll have to wash our necks!'

'Say please and thank you!'

'Do sums!'

'Learn tables!'

'We wouldn't have a life of our own at all!'

'We wouldn't be free!'

'But we aren't free down here!' said the dissenting voice of a boy known as Cur. 'If we don't steal we die of hunger, but if we *do* steal we're hanged. Where's the freedom in that? I'm going with him,' he added, and watched his friends step away from him suspiciously.

One by one they began to slide off into the gathering

shadows, merging into the darkness of the familiar alleys where they felt safe again. Soon there were only four of them left, standing in a forlorn little group in the centre of the deserted square.

'Where are they all?' cried the king frantically.

'Perhaps,' suggested the Chamberlain hopefully, 'the others don't want to come.'

'But I have so much love to give,' protested the king. 'Quite enough for all of them, if only . . .' Then he looked at the four white, pinched little faces. 'Come along my dears,' he said, gently shepherding them towards the door of his coach. 'I've got a party waiting up there in the palace for you.'

A few weeks later the Lord Chamberlain was able to enjoy telling the Knights of the Octagonal Table that he had been right all along. The king was not looking happy at all.

'Your Majesty,' said the Lord Chamberlain, in an effort to cheer him up, 'surely it's not surprising their Royal Highnesses are taking a while to settle in. After all, it must be a very big change for them!'

But the king still looked worried. 'I'm sure we wouldn't have these problems,' he said sadly, 'if only they could all realise just how much I love them.'

Grovel was the smallest of the new princes. He sidled round the palace hiding in shadowy doorways, under tables or behind curtains. His eyes were always fixed on the floor, and when the king approached him he cowered away, expecting nothing but kicks and blows.

'I'm not really a prince,' he told himself nervously. 'If the king knew what I used to do down in the city he'd have me thrown out of here – right into a dungeon.' When he was put to bed at night, he would creep out of his cosy four-poster as soon as the lights were out and lie naked on the cold stone floor. 'I was born a worthless beggar,' he would tell himself. 'I'll always be a beggar; I don't deserve to be a prince.' He never played with the fabulous toys that filled his room, gifts from his doting father, and he refused to eat the tasty food served to him on golden dishes at mealtimes. Instead he nibbled a crust of bread, while the nourishing food turned cold in front of him.

'Grovel dear,' pleaded the king, 'please look at me.' But poor Grovel never dared to lift his eyes to the king's face. If only he had, he would have seen the love in his father's eyes and the smile of approval on his face. Slowly he grew frailer, and after one particularly cold night on his bedroom floor he developed pneumonia and died.

'Oh dear,' cried the king. 'I had so much love to give to him . . . if only . . .'

The palace servants privately christened the only girl in the new royal family Princess Want-a-lot, but they never let the king hear them use that name. Right from the start she 'took' to being a princess and ordered everyone about imperiously, including the Lord Chamberlain himself. Yet in the king's presence she was as sweet as a pink sugar mouse.

'She's trying to twist him round her little finger,' growled the Lord Chamberlain as he watched the princess sitting on the king's lap, lisping into his royal ear.

'I really would love a new little coronet – made of rubies to go with my new red dress.' There was no end to her wants and wishes!

'But this is the third new outfit you've had in a week,' the king would say doubtfully.

'Daddy,' she cooed, 'you just aren't used to girls, are you? I know you'll give it to me, because you love me so much!' And of course he did. As time went on, however, her demands became so outrageous even the king became uneasy.

'Daddy darling,' she coaxed one day. 'I would so love to have my own little coach, made of silver and diamonds, so I can drive myself round the streets where I used to live – show off my new clothes to all my old friends – let them see how lucky I am.'

'No,' said the king gently, 'that would be rather vulgar, my dear. I love you too much to let you do that.' In a rage she jumped off his lap and stamped her foot.

'You don't love me!' she screamed. 'You're rich enough to give me anything I want but you keep saying no! Living with you is one long "thou shalt not!" I'm told to be good, be kind, be nice and I'm sick of it!' She locked herself in her room and ate six large boxes of sweetmeats, one after another. She exploded, of course, and the poor king was so sad he cried for days and kept on saying, 'I had so much love to give. But she didn't want my love, only my gifts . . . if only . . .'

Cur, the boy who had spoken up so bravely in the square, was quite unlike the others. In fact, he eventually became my great grandfather.

'You can't possibly be called Cur,' his new father told him. 'How terrible to brand a boy with such a dreadful name! I will give you a new name, and a new reputation to go with it! You will be called Coeur de Lion from now on. Not vicious, scavenging dog but Lion Heart! That suits you far better!'

'I'll make him love me,' thought the prince, swelling with pride. 'I'll be the best prince ever!' And he was! He worked tirelessly at his Latin, maths and military history. He got up at five to practise archery and sword fighting and he rode every horse in the royal stables with fearless skill. Soon everyone in the palace respected and admired him enormously.

'Coeur de Lion, how about a game of drafts this evening?' the king would often ask wistfully.

'Sorry, Father,' the conscientious prince would reply, 'got an essay to finish.'

As the years passed it was always the same.

'Come for a walk with me in the garden, son?'

'Sorry, can't stop, Father, must talk to the knights. We're off to quell the rising in the north at first light.'

'But you never have time to sit and talk to me,' the king would say sadly. If Coeur de Lion was not leading an army into battle, he was sailing off with the fleet to plunder far-off lands for his father's glory.

'I have endless servants who'll do all this for me,' said the king, 'but you are my son; I love you and I want to be with you.'

'Sorry, Father, can't stop now.' The reply was always the same. 'I'll make you love me yet.'

'But I *do* love you,' sighed the king. 'There is nothing you could possibly do that would make me love you any more than I already do. And nothing you could ever do that would make me love you any less.' But by the time he had said all that, Coeur de Lion had hurried away on his next important errand.

Then there was Fred.

No one ever called him Prince Fred because he never managed to look like a prince. His teeth stuck out, and so did his ears. Spots covered his face and his hair grew in defiant tufts all over his head. Whenever he tried to ride a horse he fell straight off; he never managed to make the champagne bottle smash when he launched a ship; he could not make a speech to save his life, but – oh how he loved the king!

'Just to think,' he would murmur ecstatically, 'a great ruler like you wanting a beggar like me for a son.' He was happiest when he was sitting on a stool near the throne gazing adoringly at his father or running simple little errands for him. Every day they walked together in the garden, enjoying the flowers and sharing secret jokes; each night after supper they played drafts and made toast by the fire. When the king finally lay dying, Prince Coeur de Lion was fighting some battle over the sea, but Fred sat by the bed holding his father's hand.

'The great achievements of your brother Coeur de Lion will go down in all the history books,' said the king. 'But Fred, it has been you who has brought joy to my heart.'

'But Father,' protested Fred, 'I've never done anything special for you.'

'You loved me,' murmured the king, 'and that is all I ever wanted you to do.'

'Sir, was that story true?' asked Paxalom's son gravely.

'Did it really happen like that?'

'Perhaps not quite,' admitted his father. And taking Queen Sophia's hand in his, he added, 'But didn't you know that however great a king may be, the thing he wants most is love?'

5

Cedric's Sword

Whom have I in heaven but you? And earth has
nothing I desire besides you. My flesh and my
heart may fail, but God is the strength of
my heart and my portion for ever. (Psalm
73:25–26)

'This is outrageous!' said Sir Marmaduke. Never before had
the Knights of the Octagonal Table been quite so angry
with their king. 'He can't knight a man like that and expect
us to welcome him to the Table!'

'He's so old,' added Sir Roger. 'He must be at least a hundred! *And* a mere peasant! ' For once Sir Marmaduke agreed
with him. They had all gathered in the royal ante-chamber,
to enjoy a mug of ale before the Monday council meeting.

Sir Cedric, the new knight, sat in the corner and
watched them from a distance. Fortunately, he was too deaf
to hear what they were saying. He knew they did not like
him, but during his ninety-five years of life very few people
ever had. He had indeed been born a peasant in the days

when King Paxalom's grandfather ruled the empire. He was the youngest son of a poor farm labourer, and both his parents worked hard all day cultivating other people's land. When their sons were old enough they joined them – all except Cedric, who stayed at home. His chest wheezed and puffed and his spindly little legs didn't seem strong enough to carry him far. His mother told him to make himself useful about the house, adding unkindly, 'Pity you weren't born a girl, then at least you might be worth your keep.'

Cedric hated sweeping floors and laying fires because in that rasping chest of his beat the brave heart of a soldier.

One cold winter afternoon, as he stirred the turnip stew ready for his family's evening meal, a tap on the door startled him. An old woman, huddled in rags and bent double with arthritis, crouched on the step.

'I smelled the cooking,' she said, sniffing hungrily. 'Could you spare an old woman a bowl of broth?' Cedric looked doubtful. He knew there was exactly the right amount of food in the pot, one bowl for each member of the family, and after a long day in the cold wind they would be furious if there was not a full share for each of them.

'I'm sorry . . .' he began, then noticed how thin she was and how blue her face looked in the half-light. 'You have my helping,' he said. 'I guess you need it more than I do.' Thankfully she sank down by the fire and soon emptied the bowl Cedric handed her, wiping it clean with the hunk of black bread that should have been his supper. Content at last, she lay back against the log pile and closed her eyes.

Cedric anxiously watched the watery sun dip behind the woods, knowing the rest of the family would be home at dusk and would not want to find a stranger by their hearth.

'Poor old thing,' he thought, and wondered how he could bear to turn her out into the frost. Suddenly she opened her old eyes and looked at him.

'What do you most want, boy?' she demanded. 'What's your dream?'

'That's easy,' laughed Cedric, without giving the matter a thought. 'I want to be a knight. I want to grow up brave and strong and fight for my king, protect him by some act of bravery – perhaps even save his life and . . .'

'Hold on, boy,' interrupted the old crone, 'that's quite enough for one lifetime!' Hobbling to the door she fetched in what Cedric had taken to be her walking staff. Carefully she began to unwind the strips of rag that covered not a stick but a sword in a leather scabbard.

'It belonged to my father,' she said at last, as she slid the blade free of its sheath and ran its steely expanse across the back of her hand. 'He was a Knight of the Table, wounded in battle and brought home to die. He gave me his sword and told me to keep it carefully until I found a man who was worthy of it. My life's been hard and I've lost every-thing I ever had except the sword. Now I think, at long last, I've found someone who will use it. Keep its blade sharp and one day you will use it to defend your king.'

Cedric only just had time to thank her, hide the sword under his straw pallet and hustle her out of the cottage before his family could be heard tramping home through the woods.

'Come back whenever you like,' he whispered before she disappeared into the shadows, but he never saw her again.

Cedric knew he must keep his sword a secret, as his

father and brothers would sell it and drink its price. But every day when the chores were done he practised with it. If anyone had ever seen him they would have laughed at the sight of a tiny figure slashing at hay bales with such a massive sword. However, no blade was ever better oiled or more lovingly honed.

All this daily exercise strengthened Cedric's legs and cured his wheezing. Although he never grew very much, he soon joined his brothers in the fields.

'One day I'm going to be a soldier,' he would insist. But they only laughed.

When Cedric became a man he set off for the palace, ready to join the king's own bodyguard.

'Sorry, but you're just too small,' the sergeant told him.

'But I've got a sword!' said Cedric, drawing it dramatically from its sheath.

'It's too big for a mouse like you,' laughed the sergeant, and all the other soldiers joined in the joke.

'You wait!' Cedric replied. 'When there's a war, you won't care how short I am – you'll be glad of a sword like mine!'

'What good's a sword these days?' said the sergeant. King Paxalom's grandfather had been such a great statesman that peace reigned in the land throughout his entire life, but that did not stop Cedric. He practised fencing every single day because he was so sure that eventually the king would need him. 'I'll be a knight yet,' he told himself.

As the years went by he worked so hard in the fields that he was made Farm Overseer with a little cottage of his own, and a fireplace over which to hang his sword. Every evening after work he carefully took it down to polish and sharpen its deadly blade.

'What's the point of doing all that?' scolded his wife. 'Why don't you sell the ridiculous old thing? The king's never going to need you now!'

'Well, I'll be ready for him if he does,' Cedric would reply quietly.

When his children were small they believed every word of his story, and listened with open mouths and big round eyes. When they were teenagers they stopped listening and laughed instead.

'You, a knight?' they would mock. 'The king would never need a midget like you. Don't you know he's a giant?'

On market days he always wore his sword when he went to town to sell the eggs and cheese.

'Here comes Sir Cedric, Defender of the King!' people would shout, and a shower of rotten eggs and apples always came his way.

'You'll see me knighted one day,' he would mutter as he wiped his smock. He never used his sword to defend himself but vented his rage on the way home by swiping and slashing the unfortunate gorse bushes that he passed along the way.

Years went by, but even when Cedric was a great grandfather, snoozing by the hearth, he always kept his sword sharp and his wrist supple.

'It's time you gave up this silly dream, Grandpa,' said his youngest granddaughter when times were hard one cold winter. 'You're nearly a hundred! If you sold your sword you'd keep us all clothed and fed for a year.'

'Even old men can serve their king,' replied Cedric firmly.

In the spring that same year Cedric was asleep in his

chair, with his shaky old hands folded on his bony knees, when the sound of horses galloping through the woods woke him with a start. Hastily he buckled on his sword and shuffled painfully to the door. A group of riders emerged from the trees, and at their head, on a huge white horse, was King Paxalom himself. Cedric had never seen him before, but recognised him at once. 'Just like his grandfather,' he said with satisfaction.

'Have you seen anyone else pass this way today, good sir?' asked Paxalom politely. Cedric was too overcome with emotion to speak as he stiffly knelt to kiss the king's hand. 'We have been riding hard since daybreak,' continued the king. 'Would you mind if my men let their horses drink from your duck pond?' Cedric answered with a low bow that almost proved too much for his arthritis.

'One of my barons tried to murder me last night,' explained Paxalom. 'He is not an evil man, just sick in his mind. He ran away when we tried to restrain him, but I fear he is extremely dangerous and may try to kill again if we do not catch him soon. So do beware, my friend, if he should come this way.'

Cedric bowed again and, as the king's companions watered their horses, he found himself chatting to Paxalom about the turnip crop and the weather. It was while they were laughing together like old friends that Cedric noticed the bushes shivering suspiciously, just behind the king's horse, even though there was no wind that day. As he watched he saw a man peer out at the king, and caught the glint of metal. Cedric's old face never changed. He went on talking about late frosts and apple blossom, but he began to edge his way slowly round the horse's head until he was between the animal and the bushes. Then suddenly he unsheathed his sword, swung round and lunged towards the assassin just as he raised his dagger to strike the king. Taken completely off guard by the totally unexpected speed of the old man he had taken for a dotard, the baron's aim was ruined and, instead of killing the king, the dagger merely gashed Cedric's shoulder. Unchecked by the wound, the old man lunged again and before the murderer had time to reach for his second dagger the blade of Cedric's sword had struck its fatal blow. Both men sank to the ground together and were soon surrounded by the king's companions and Cedric's astonished granddaughter.

'Whatever have you done now, Grandpa?' she exclaimed. 'I told you to sell that silly sword!'

'Had he heeded you, mistress,' murmured Paxalom, 'I would be the one lying dead in your garden.' Hastily he dismounted and knelt on the grass beside Cedric. 'Are you badly hurt, Sir Knight?' he asked gently.

'Just a scratch,' replied the old man. 'I fear it's only my rheumatics that pin me to the ground.' As the king helped him to his feet, the old man looked troubled. 'Your Majesty, I am a little hard of hearing, but I thought you called me Sir Knight. I fear I am only a humble farm worker.'

Paxalom bent to pick up Cedric's sword, examining it appreciatively. 'Yet you wield your sword as bravely as any knight I know,' he said simply.

'All my life I've longed to be a knight,' replied Cedric, 'but it is honour enough to have served Your Majesty today.'

'I think not,' smiled Paxalom, and there and then he dubbed him knight with his own sword.

'So, Gentlemen,' said Paxalom as he opened the council meeting the following Monday morning. 'I see you do not approve of our new knight, Sir Cedric.' There was an embarrassed pause while they all remembered the king's uncomfortable knack of knowing what other people were thinking!

'We feel it is a little unfair, sire,' replied Sir Marmaduke cautiously, 'that someone who has done so little should be given such a great honour.'

'So you consider saving my life a little thing?' said Paxalom, amused.

'Of course not, sire,' blustered Sir Marmaduke, 'but the rest of us have achieved so much over the years: fought your battles, quelled rebellions, slain dragons and won so many great victories. We have served you all our lives.'

'And I am deeply grateful, gentlemen, for all that you have done,' said Paxalom gently, 'but Sir Cedric would have done all that too, had he been given the chance. It is not how much a knight actually does for his king that matters but how much he is *willing* to do, and whether he stays willing right to the very end.'

So, for the last three years of his life, Sir Cedric spent his days sitting happily in the royal courtyard, telling his story to anyone who would listen and oiling his faithful sword. He was never called upon to use it again but, as he lay dying, he gave it to Paxalom, who wore it proudly and used it to win many great battles.

6

The Secret Room

> If we claim to be without sin, we deceive our-
> selves and the truth is not in us. If we confess
> our sins, he is faithful and just and will forgive
> us our sins and purify us from all unrighteous-
> ness. (1 John 1:8–9)

When King Paxalom was thrown from his horse, people
said how good it was that the accident should happen so
close to Good Mother Susan's house. King Paxalom did
not agree. To him there was nothing good about falling off
a horse!

He had been hunting in the forest with some friends,
but without success, and was returning late in the afternoon, cold, wet and hungry. Paxalom was so tired he may
even have drifted off to sleep in the saddle when his horse
stumbled on a rabbit hole and threw him to the ground.
He was up again instantly, more concerned for his horse
than himself, but his right shoulder soon began to hurt
badly.

Almost the entire population of the nearby village appeared at once.

'Good Mother Susan will soon put His Majesty right,' they agreed. 'What a good thing he fell off just here!'

'I'd rather go straight home,' said Paxalom. The peasants shook their heads in disbelief; obviously they felt that the treat of being cared for by their Good Mother was something he could not miss.

'She nurses us all when we're ill – and feeds the poor!'

'There isn't a baby in these parts she hasn't delivered,' put in someone else.

'And she's ever so good at laying out the dead,' finished an old hag, eyeing Paxalom speculatively.

'Is there no end to her virtues?' he snapped crossly as the hunting party was firmly led towards a farmhouse on the outskirts of the village.

'She'll welcome you,' they told him, as they pushed open the garden gate. 'She always takes in waifs and strays.' Paxalom had to smile in spite of his shoulder.

He just had time to notice an immaculate garden, with vegetables standing to attention in weed-free rows, before he was confronted by the paragon herself. She looked as perfect as her garden.

The smile she gave her distinguished visitors, as she ushered them proudly inside, could not have been more gracious if she had been a queen. Yet there was something about her that made Paxalom uneasy. 'That smile is hiding something,' he thought. 'Perhaps she is not quite as perfect as she wants everyone to believe.'

It was a relief to sink back into the big armchair by the fire; his shoulder was more painful than he cared to admit.

The kitchen, which was obviously the main room of the house, looked as immaculate as its mistress; and the copper pans hanging around the hearth gleamed with frequent polishing. Four little girls stood in a row, eyeing the king respectfully. They looked so tidy and well behaved they could have been made from wax, but there was nothing passive about Dame Susan. She and her servant moved at high speed, seeing to everyone's comfort. While the girl served soup to his friends, Susan ran her deft fingers over the king's shoulder.

'No bones broken,' she pronounced, 'but the muscles are badly wrenched. I'll brew something for the pain, Your Majesty.'

He watched her as she chopped herbs and other mysterious ingredients into a cauldron hanging over the fire, smiling pleasantly all the time. As she finally handed him the concoction, however, he noticed that her eyes were full of darkness. Was it sorrow, he wondered, or a much stronger emotion?

'Try to sleep, Majesty,' she said kindly. 'Your horse is unhurt and enjoying hay in my stable. If you give the medicine time your ride home will be much less painful.' It was quiet in the kitchen now; two of his friends had ridden home to warn the queen of his late arrival and the others were out with the horses. Even the four wax model children had been marched away in a smart line by the servant. But Paxalom was wide awake – his curiosity having roused him.

'Thank you, Good Mother,' he said, 'but will you sit with me a while? I would prefer to talk than sleep.'

She did not look pleased, and sat down stiffly on the

edge of a chair as far away from him as possible.

'Your husband?' he asked tentatively.

'He was far older than me,' she replied with a shrug. 'He could have been my father. He died years ago, but I have managed the farm ever since and we prosper. My labourers respect me.'

'I have been told by almost everyone in your village how well you have done and how good you are.' She looked genuinely delighted at that.

'What would you say is your most precious possession?' asked Paxalom, and without hesitation she replied, 'My reputation, sire.'

'Yes, "Good Mother" is a perfect title; but why does it matter so much to you that others see you as good?'

She looked startled, and retorted almost angrily, 'Surely being good is important!'

'So it is,' replied Paxalom. 'Far more important than being *seen* to be good.'

'I must close the shutters,' she said, rising hastily to hide her scarlet cheeks. Many curious faces peered in through the windows as the entire village assembled to see their local saint entertaining the king. They looked most upset when she shut them out.

'You have no sons to ease your burden?' To his surprise, Paxalom saw a shaft of fear shoot across her face when he had been expecting sadness. What was it, he wondered, that haunted this admirable woman and spoiled the contentment she obviously deserved?

'I have no sons, sire,' she replied woodenly. 'In fact I have no children of my own. The four little girls were all waifs and strays until I took them in.'

She went on talking about the orphans at great length, until Paxalom realised she was using her anecdotes to distract his attention. For some reason he never quite understood, he said, 'Mistress, I think you *do* have a child.'

She recoiled as if he had slapped her. 'Please,' she whispered, 'I know you have many strange powers, but have mercy and leave this be!' She was twisting her hands miserably under her starched white apron.

'You are a nurse! You must know that sometimes, in order to bring healing, it is necessary to lance a poisonous wound, however painful that may feel,' said the king softly. 'Show me your son, Good Mother.'

'But I am *not* good!' she almost shouted, and her fingers instinctively clutched a large iron key that hung from her waist.

Risking a guess, Paxalom said, 'Unlock the door for me, mistress.'

'The thing must stay hidden,' she said in anguish. 'It would be better for everyone.'

'Susan, it would not be better for *you*.' It was the tenderness in his voice that broke her, and anyway she knew that kings have to be obeyed. Sobbing brokenly she made sure there were no cracks left at the windows, then she hurried to bar three of the doors that led from the room. Finally she pushed open the fourth and held it wide for the king to pass through.

The room was obviously her bedchamber, but the windows were boarded up.

'No one is allowed to see into this room,' she muttered, 'and no one else ever comes here.'

Paxalom, still light-headed from the potion, leaned

against the bedpost while she pulled a high oak settle away from the wall by the fireplace. It slid out so easily it must have been mounted on hidden wheels. Behind it was a small door.

'Sire,' she said, turning in final appeal, 'please have mercy.'

'Let me help you,' said Paxalom, putting a hand on her shoulder. 'This is more than you can do alone.' Unwillingly she turned the key and, picking up her candle, she pushed the door open.

Paxalom had to crouch down to peer into what was little more than a large dark cupboard. The guttering candle-light revealed a tragic scene. On a small pallet in the corner lay the twisted form of an emaciated child, who looked at them from a wizened face – more like a hairless skull. The limbs twitched and waved about aimlessly as he mewed like a wounded kitten.

Paxalom squeezed through the narrow door, ignoring the pain from his shoulder, and knelt down beside the mat-tress. The child gazed up at him and then, quite suddenly, he smiled. Paxalom put out one enormous finger, which the child tried to grasp, but without success.

'All it can do of its own will is smile,' said Susan bitterly.

'May I bring your son out to sit with me by the kitchen fire?' asked Paxalom. 'Will you lift him for me?'

Dame Susan looked horrified. 'It's never been out of here in its life!' she protested. 'Not since the day it was born. No one else knows it exists! What would they all think?'

'You locked all the doors, mistress – no one will come.'

She still protested, but kings have to be obeyed, so a few

moments later Paxalom was cradling the fragile body on his knee, while the child continued to smile up into his face.

'Why are you so ashamed of such a special son?' he asked softly.

'He was sent to curse me for my sin and bring shame on the whole house,' she cried. 'He's fourteen! But look at him!'

'You have a wide reputation for caring for the sick,' he said. 'You would not lock your own son permanently in a dark prison unless you were ashamed of something more than crippled limbs.'

'I wanted him to die!' she muttered viciously. 'Every day I expected him to die; but he's so stubborn. He's my punishment.'

'But you must have fed and cared for him all the same?' said Paxalom.

'My husband said I was a fool, but it's in me to heal and nourish.'

Something that sounded like a tentative chuckle came from the child as Paxalom stroked his wrinkled forehead.

'Mistress,' he said gently, 'tell me about your son.'

She could not look into his face, so she had to turn her back as she began. 'My family were prosperous and highly respected in this village. Our farm was on the hill yonder, and I was the only child. When I was seventeen I loved the only son of this house, but he was already married to a sour-faced girl who couldn't have children.

'Our love grew too strong for us, and when he was drowned in the floods that winter, I knew I carried his child. Sire! That was the only time I ever sinned!'

Paxalom said nothing, for to him pride was the worst sin of all.

'I could not be disgraced before the whole community! I thought it would be better to throw myself into the same river that had taken my man from me. As I stood there, his father came up behind me. He had a cold stone for a heart! He only cared about his farm and who could carry it on after him. I wanted to hurt him, so I told him I carried his son's child but intended to drown it. How he wanted that baby! "He is the heir to my land!" he said and, since his own wife had died, he asked me to marry him. "It will make the child respectable," he said, but I saw that marriage would also cover my shame.

'We were wed soon afterwards, but I deceived him into thinking it was at least six more months until my baby would come — I was a very plump girl then. However, it was only the day after our wedding, and our guests had hardly departed when my pains began. I was so afraid of the disgrace, and all the gossip, that I would not have the midwife. I planned to hide the baby for a while, but when it was born, we saw it was a cripple. My husband said it had been sent to curse us!

'"Leave it alone to die," he told me. "It's no good to me!" So we put it in that cupboard until morning. It was so weak and limp I never expected it to move when I went to fetch it away to the river before first light. It was warm in the cupboard because it lies behind the fire, and the baby still lived, so I suckled it — I couldn't stop myself. I kept telling my husband it would die soon, but it never has!' Her whole face twisted with pain. 'Let me put it away again before anyone sees!'

Paxalom looked down at the child who was trying so hard to make himself understood.

'Inside this frail body is a mind and a very brave spirit,' said the king. 'See how he wants to speak to us. In time I think he will surprise us with how many things he learns to do.'

'But sire,' she wailed, 'how am I going to explain . . . what will people say?'

Then a strange expression touched her face. 'Sire, I have heard that you have magic drops that cure all ills,' she said eagerly. 'Would you give one to it . . . to my son?'

'Are you saying that you will only love him if he is fit and well – useful to you on the farm?' asked Paxalom. 'Love that makes conditions is no love at all. He needs you to love and enjoy him just as he is. And mistress,' he added, 'I believe that you *have* loved him – since the day you first suckled him. You have cared for him for fourteen years in almost impossible circumstances. Only love brings commitment like that – but I think you have loved your reputation even more.'

'Could I tell people that I found it, this evening, on the back step – left by gypsies?'

Paxalom laughed and shook his head. 'No, you have lived with lies and darkness in your heart for too long. Now it is time for you to be truly good, instead of only being seen to be good. Come, sit here with your son while I call his sisters to meet him.'

The four little girls melted exactly as if they really had been made of wax, and smiled, cried and kissed the brother who seemed more like a doll to them.

'Is he really ours?' asked the youngest.

'Did you give him to us?' added the older one.

'Yes, perhaps I did in a way,' smiled the king. 'But I like him so much, I would like to keep a little bit of him for myself, if that's all right with you.'

Then he crossed to the windows and flung open the shutters. Out in the darkness there must have been at least a hundred villagers trampling the dame's vegetables and herbs.

'Come in, good people,' called the king. 'I have news for you.' They surged in through the door and packed themselves tightly into every corner of the kitchen. 'Mother Susan has for some years been bravely and skilfully nurturing her crippled child in secret because she thought he was a curse sent to blight her family, but I have convinced her that, instead, he is a blessing and will bring healing as well as joy to us all . . .' His speech was interrupted at that moment by the approach of many horses, and the crowd round the door gasped in astonishment as Queen Sophia herself swept into the house.

'Paxalom!' she said with a despairing smile. 'Whatever are you doing now?'

'I am about to introduce you to . . .' He stopped and looked down at Dame Susan. 'What did you say the child is called?' he whispered. She flushed and bit her lip, unable to admit he never had a name. Paxalom understood instantly and said, 'This is Paxalom. He bears a king's name because he has an unconquerable spirit! In fact,' he added, picking up his discarded sword, 'there is something else I was about to do.' Very gently he touched the two fragile shoulders with the tip of his sword and said, 'I dub you knight. You shall be called Sir Paxalom, Proud Son of

Susan.' Everyone clapped and cheered while the queen shook her head, quite bewildered.

And Sir Paxalom did bring healing to his mother's heart, and soon the farmhouse was full of laughter at his antics. When his sisters had homes of their own he brought comfort to his mother in her old age. King Paxalom gave him a tiny horse with a special saddle and every day he was lifted on to its back to roam round the village, smiling at everyone he met. The king even had a minute suit of armour made for him to wear on special occasions, with a little silver sword to match. The fact that he could not hold it did not matter at all because, as his mother often said, 'It is what is in your heart that counts the most.'

7

The Sweet-maker

Remain in me, and I will remain in you. No
branch can bear fruit by itself; it must remain
in the vine. Neither can you bear fruit unless
you remain in me. (John 15:4)

'I think I shall go mad,' cried King Paxalom, 'unless I have
some peace and silence soon!' He was in the middle of an
extensive royal tour around his eastern provinces. He had
been travelling continuously from one crowded town to
the next, smiling at cheering crowds and listening to boring speeches from pompous barons. Grumbling governors
had complained to him endlessly, and wherever he went
streams of people tried to attract his attention. Their peti-
tions, demands for justice and requests for money were
endless. Then there were the sick, standing in long, patient
lines, desperately hoping for his help. He always touched
every one of them; many were healed but all were comforted.

'I think I'll take a few days off,' said Paxalom when
his entourage arrived at the foot of a magnificent range

of mountains. 'I need to go hunting.'

'I'll come too,' said Sir Roger eagerly. Paxalom sighed. Silence and Sir Roger did not go together, but he hadn't the heart to leave him behind.

'I too will accompany Your Majesty,' said Sir Marmaduke sounding like a condemned martyr. 'I cannot trust Sir Roger to take proper care of your royal person.' Paxalom smiled. He knew there was only one thing his crusty old knight hated more than hunting, and that was being separated from his king.

At dawn the following morning they set off with just a few servants and a pack of hunting dogs. The king hardly spoke all day as the horses picked their way up the steep mountain paths. By evening the forest trees had been left far below and the rugged peaks lay before them.

'We must be miles from the nearest house,' sighed Sir Marmaduke gloomily.

'No! Look up there,' replied Sir Roger, who could never resist the chance to put someone right. 'It looks like a large village perched up there on that rocky shelf.'

'Perhaps we could stay there for the night,' suggested Sir Marmaduke hopefully. He loathed campfires and tents.

The shadows were already long by the time they had climbed the precipitous path and finally ridden through the walls that surrounded the village. The silence that met them was eerie.

'Where is everybody?' demanded Sir Marmaduke in disgust. The streets were deserted and the only living creatures they could see were the sparrows that hopped in and out of abandoned houses.

'How strange,' said Sir Roger. 'These are not the

dwellings of poor mountain peasants; they're too large and grand. Very rich people must have lived here.'

'But why would the wealthy build houses up here, so far from civilization?' shuddered Sir Marmaduke.

'And why did they all leave so suddenly?' added the king.

'It's ghostly,' said the older knight. 'Even a tent would be better than sleeping here!'

Once Paxalom had ordered Sir Marmaduke not to grumble and Sir Roger not to talk, the days in the mountains were a great success – even if the hunting was not! When they finally rode back down to the valley to face the clamouring crowds, King Paxalom asked the local baron what he knew about the deserted village. 'Does no one live there now?'

'Oh yes, sire,' was his reply. 'Three people would have been watching you all the time, but they have good cause to hide from strangers.'

By asking many questions all over the busy market town, Paxalom gradually pieced together a strange story that he told to Queen Sophia the night he finally reached home. They were having a quiet supper together in their private garden, and she was so pleased to see him home that she sat gazing into his face, hardly taking in a word he said.

'The place was once nothing but a group of huts belonging to some poor peasants, who just managed to survive by hunting and keeping goats. Then one day a Holy Man arrived and built himself a shelter. They decided he *must* be holy because he sat still all day, doing nothing at all – except holding out his hands to the sun.

"Why do you sit like that?" they asked him.

'"I'm communing with my maker," he would reply, so they told each other he was mad as well as holy, and left him alone.'

After many years of sitting like that, all day long, the Holy Man discovered that a film of sweetness would form on his palms by the evening. As he waited quietly it hardened into a crust, like spun sugar, and he would roll it into little balls, which he laid out on the stone slab beside him.

He began to offer these sweets to the children who always came to stare at him. They loved them and brought their friends to try them too. The more children who came the more sweetness the old man's palms produced.

'What's he giving our children?' the women asked each other suspiciously, and they all went to the Holy Man and asked for some too.

'It's no good coming in the morning,' he told them. 'I have to commune with my maker all day before the sweetness comes.' So the women came back in the evening, shooing the children away with their broomsticks.

'No, no,' said the Holy Man, 'there's plenty for everyone.'

They liked the sweets so much they came every evening, but it took the men a long time before they condescended to come too, and longer still before they admitted there was a miracle-worker in their village.

However, in time, everyone used to gather at sunset outside the Holy Man's hut, and soon people were claiming the sweets had made them well, and much stronger than they had ever been before.

Villagers who lived lower down the mountain began

trudging up the steep track to join the crowd at the end of the day. Even though they had to slither back home in the dark, they were always convinced it was worth the effort.

'You shouldn't give our sweets to all these strangers!' complained the village chief. 'You won't have enough left for us.'

'Let them come,' smiled the Holy Man. 'I want to help them too; there will be enough.' But the chief was still not pleased.

'We should charge them,' he told the other men. 'These sweets are *ours.*'

When they told the Holy Man about the chief's idea, he was horrified.

'How can we make people pay for what was given to us as a gift?' he asked. So the chief had a wall built round the village and, without telling the Holy Man, he charged strangers to come through the gate. Still they came, more of them every day, but they were too poor to pay in anything but eggs, cheese or wool. The villagers thought these were luxuries, until the chief had a better idea.

'We must sell our sweets in the market down in the valley where people would pay us in real money,' he decided. So the men made wooden boxes, the women decorated them and the chief filled them with sweets. The pilgrims beat plaintively on the gates and the village children cried bitterly, but they were all firmly told the sweets must be given to people who needed them more than they did.

The Holy Man was sad when he heard the crying and the knocking, but he forced himself to take no notice because there were so many people living down there in the valley who needed his sweets to brighten up their lives.

When the chief had finished building himself a grand new house he had another idea: 'The people who have been buying our sweets in the valley market are farmers and tradesmen who only have coppers to spend. We should send our miracle sweets to the great markets of the world.' So they made bigger and more elaborately designed boxes and soon camel trains were setting off in all directions, returning laden with gold.

Soon all the villagers had grand houses – except the Holy Man, who was quite content, communing with his maker. People all over the world were talking about the miraculous 'Mountain Sweets', but only the richest could afford to sample them.

'Isn't it wonderful!' the chief told the Holy Man. 'Now your sweetness is reaching sultans and emperors, and making them fit and well!' The Holy Man was very pleased indeed.

These illustrious customers demanded more sweets for their many wives and concubines and, of course, their innumerable children all wanted some too.

'We cannot make enough to satisfy them all!' the chief told the Holy Man. 'Couldn't you manage to produce a bit more each day?'

'I'll try,' replied the Holy Man, and he tried so hard that he frowned with the effort instead of smiling up into the sun as he always had before.

The more the orders arrived, the more tense the villagers became, and every time the Holy Man settled down to commune with his maker someone would come and interrupt him. 'Try a little bit harder,' they would say.

'Surely you want to help people all over the world?' The Holy Man did, but the more he was disturbed, the less sweetness was produced.

So the chief tried another idea.

'The trouble is, you're not near enough to the sun,' he told the Holy Man, and he had a high wooden tower built so he could sit right up at the very top. At first the Holy Man was delighted, but every five minutes the chief would send someone up the ladder to see how he was getting on.

'You mustn't let them pressure me like this,' he told the chief.

'We're only trying to encourage you,' was the reply. 'We keep thinking of all those poor people who've never yet had the chance to taste your sweets. Don't you care about them?' The Holy Man cared about them so much he found his hands were trembling, which made it harder to hold them out to the sun.

'Here's an idea!' said the chief. 'Suppose I sit beside you? You could rest your hands in my lap and I could roll the sweets for you. Surely that would make things much quicker?'

The Holy Man did his best not to mind, but the chief kept talking all day long. Because he had no peace to commune with his maker, the film grew thinner still.

Then the chief had his best idea ever. When the Holy Man had his eyes closed, communing, he added chalk dust to the sweetness to make it go further. However, he had to add more each day because the sweetness was diminishing so rapidly.

And one day there was none at all.

The Holy Man was so upset he fell off his tower and

had to be carried home to bed.

'I know what we'll do,' said the chief. 'We'll add honey to the chalk dust until he gets better.'

Soon the sweets that filled the fancy boxes were only mass-produced fakes.

'These Mountain Sweets don't taste as good as they used to,' said the sultans and emperors, and their children spat them out all over their marble floors.

When the camel trains stopped carrying gold coins back up the mountain, the chief banged on the door of the Holy Man's hut every morning and shouted, 'Aren't you better *yet*!' But the Holy Man wouldn't answer; he never came out into the sunshine any more.

So the discontented villagers packed their many possessions and moved away, leaving their great houses empty and derelict and their stores filled with boxes of uneaten sweets.

When he was sure everyone had gone, the Holy Man crept out of his hut and sat down, holding his hands out to the sun. When it was evening he opened his eyes and saw two little boys sitting watching him. They had been left behind because they were cripples and no one wanted them. The Holy Man rolled them each a ball of his sweetness and then he gave the rest as a gift to his maker.

He did exactly the same every evening and, as the boys ate the sweets each day, they gradually grew straight and strong; in time they too became Holy Men. The three of them still live up there, enjoying the sun, the sweetness and their maker.

'I wish I could have met that Holy Man,' sighed Paxalom

when he finished the story. 'I think I would have liked him. What do you think, my dear?' But Queen Sophia had fallen happily asleep with her head resting on his shoulder.

8

Giants and Dwarfs

> Live in harmony with one another. Do not be
> proud, but be willing to associate with people
> of low position. (Romans 12:16)

King Paxalom was immensely proud of his only son, but
tried very hard not to show it. Prince Michael was even
more proud of his father, but he had no problem about
showing his feelings.

'My father can do anything,' he used to say, 'but I wish
he didn't have to go away quite so often.' The little boy
would stand on the battlements whenever the king rode off
on important business with his knights. He used to wave
bravely, but tears would always run down his cheeks.
Paxalom missed him badly too, so when Michael was eight
years old he took him on a state visit to one of the south-
ern provinces. The king had to choose four of their many
barons as regional governors; the trip seemed like a dull
chore to him, but to his small son it was a magnificent
adventure.

When they arrived, a vast banquet was given in their honour, and all the rich and important men in the region were invited. Each one tried to dress more grandly than the others in order to prove he was worthy of promotion. To the little prince sitting beside his father at the high table, they all looked important, and he wondered how his father would ever be able to pick four from so many hundreds.

'How can you tell which are the right men?' he asked anxiously.

'First I'll sort the giants from the dwarfs,' smiled his father.

The boy looked round the Great Hall and said, 'They all look the same size to me.' Then he smiled and added, 'You were talking in riddles again, sir! But I really *do* want to know, because one day I'll be a king myself.'

Paxalom knew how long it would take for the noble company to chew their way through all thirty-five courses that made up a royal banquet, so to delay the onset of his son's inevitable boredom, he began: 'Once upon a time . . .' The prince abandoned his struggle with the roast venison on his plate and leaned happily on the arm of his father's chair. 'When I was still a very new king I went off with a few of my friends to the Menacing Mountains for a long hunting trip.'

'The Menacing Mountains!' breathed Michael in awe. 'Weren't you frightened to go to such a dangerous place?'

'I was young then, and still a bit headstrong,' admitted Paxalom. 'I hadn't learned how menacing those mountains can be. We had only been there a day before the mists came rolling down, all damp and clammy, and we couldn't see where we were going. I was beginning to fear we would fall over a precipice, when we discovered a huge cave. "Just right to shelter in," we thought, until we realised it was not a cave – it was a tunnel.

'Like the fools we were, we *had* to see where it led, so we groped our way through the darkness for what seemed like hours. It led us right through one of the mountains and into a strange land that I never knew was there at all. The mist was gone and the sun was shining, so at first I liked the look of the place very much – until I realised who lived there!

'In the distance we saw what looked like a town, so we rode towards it in search of food and a mug of ale. But as we drew closer, we saw a very strange sight indeed. The houses were either so tall they seemed to reach the sky, or they were as tiny as your little playhouse in the garden at home. Then, out of the tall houses came the giants!'

'Were they fierce?' asked Michael hopefully.

'Well, not all of them were. The first few we met were very kind indeed. They brought us food, drink and lots of oats for our horses; and they each wanted to put us up for the night.'

'Were they really giants, Father – even taller than you?' To Michael, Paxalom was the tallest man on earth.

'Oh, they were much taller than me,' was the reply the little prince found hard to believe. 'They were ten, fifteen feet tall at least and all dressed in green. I'd always thought giants were rather horrid, but I soon found they were some of the nicest people I'd ever met. All they seemed to want to do was help us, give us advice on how to get home, explain to us about their land and make us feel at home – nothing seemed too much trouble.'

'If they lived in the tall houses,' said Michael, 'who lived in the little ones?'

'The dwarfs. There were just as many dwarfs in that land as giants – tiny little fellows, scuttling about the market-place in all directions.'

'Were they kind too?'

'Well no. They seemed to want us to be kind to *them*! They kept on running up asking for things. Some wanted money, or a ride on our horses; some even asked us to help them carry bales of cloth or milk churns for them. I have to say that I didn't like those dwarfs very much; they were always looking up at the giants trying to find one who would help them. Not that those green giants minded that – they were always looking down at the dwarfs hoping to find someone they could take care of or advise. They did all the hard work while the dwarfs just ran about getting in their way.

'There were a few dwarfs, though, who didn't seem to be looking for a friendly giant; instead they seemed afraid of them. They were so frightened of us they hid and a few even threw rotten eggs and apples from the windows of their houses. I thought they were most unfriendly, but I suppose they thought we had come to harm them, and they were only protecting themselves.

'I was just tucking in to a lovely hot dinner, which a very caring female giant had cooked for me, when more giants came pushing their way through the crowd. They were all dressed in red and were quite different from the kind giants. Bossy, that's what I called them. All the red giants wanted to do was tell people off, tell them what to do and then tell them they'd done it wrong! They all seemed to be shouting at us at once.

'"You shouldn't have risked hunting in the Menacing Mountains."

'"Why did you come barging through our tunnel without asking first?"

'"Who do you think you are anyway?"

'One of the dwarfs, who was sitting next to me, trying to persuade me to give him half my dinner, sniffed and said, "The red giants are so mean. They make us work for them like slaves – it isn't fair. And just look at that!" He pointed to two big red giants who were kicking a dwarf between them as if he were a football.

'"No wonder some of them always look so frightened," I said.

'"Yes, some poor little dwarfs always expect that every giant they meet is going to hurt them or disappoint them. So they can't seem to trust anyone. Such a pity, isn't it?"

'"Surely the green ones want to protect you?" I said.

'"Oh yes, green giants *love* coming to the rescue, but some dwarfs actually *like* the red giants because they enjoy being bossed around. They feel safer if they have someone to tell them what to do all the time. Of course, most of us prefer the kind green giants because it's so nice to have someone big and strong to take care of you, isn't it?"

'"I've never wanted to be looked after by anyone," I said. "Particularly not my grandmother."

'"That's because you're a giant inside," he said with another sniff. "All humans are either giants or dwarfs – or so I'm told."

'"Nonsense!" I laughed. "People are all roughly the same size."

' "Oh, but they're giants or dwarfs in their hearts, only you can't see the difference from the outside."

'I thought he was quite mad, and I told him so, but just then up came the biggest and bossiest red giant of them all.

' "What's all this!" he boomed, and before we could do anything he had picked me up, with my five friends, and tucked us all under one of his massive arms. "Look after their horses," he shouted over his shoulder; and of course lots of green giants, always happy to help, hurried forward at once.'

'Where did he take you?' asked Michael.

'Off to his great tall house on the outskirts of the town, and there we were, prisoners, completely in his power.'

'Was he cruel to you?' asked Michael anxiously.

'Oh no, he made us very comfortable indeed. We had lots of food and very comfortable beds. He just liked being in control and having other people in his power. We were amazed to find that his wife was a dwarf. He was very bossy and bullying to her, but she didn't seem to mind at all and rushed round after him like an adoring little dog. She had to climb a stepladder to lay the table for her husband and swing from a rope in order to make his bed! He told us that the very best and happiest marriages were always between dwarfs who needed someone to look after them or control them and giants who needed to care or control! They met each other's needs perfectly.

'After being there for a few days we soon realised that their next-door neighbours were not so well suited. They were both red giants who each wanted to be the boss! The noise they made with their constant fights and arguments kept us awake most nights!'

'How did you escape?' asked Michael.

'Our gaoler's wife helped us in the end. She wouldn't have dared to give us the key to his front door, but she hated all the extra work we made for her, so when she next went to the market, she chatted to a few of the other red giants and got them all worked up nicely. Round they came, all wanting to criticise, bully and organise. They shouted such rude things outside his door he had to let us go in the end. By that time I couldn't wait to get out of that crazy land.'

'So how did you ever find the way home?' asked Michael.

'That was quite an adventure too!' laughed Paxalom. 'We tried asking dwarfs, but the helpless kind only wanted us to chop logs for them, or give them a ride home with their shopping; the frightened sort hid in the bushes and threw stones at us. If we asked the kind green giants they wanted to keep us as pets, while the bossy giants told us off for wanting to leave. In the end we found two green giants who obviously loved rescuing people; they managed to find our horses and, at dead of night, they led us back to the tunnel. We were halfway to the far side when we heard the red giants pounding after us. "Come back! You belong to us!"

'We couldn't make our horses gallop in that dark tunnel, so the giants gained on us rapidly. Fortunately they kept hitting their heads on the roof of the cave and falling over each other. So we finally managed to escape and I've never gone back to the Menacing Mountains since – unless I absolutely had to!'

'I liked that story,' said the prince, as his neglected

venison was removed and replaced by a wobbling jelly. 'But I think it was actually one of your made-up ones, wasn't it, Father?' Paxalom smiled and admitted his son was right.

'But there is a lot of truth in it,' he added. 'When you grow up, remember that most human beings are either "giants" or "dwarfs" on the inside. Giants enjoy looking down on other people, either because they're kind and want to help or because they're bossy and want to criticise or control. You'll meet a lot of dwarfs too, always looking up at the giants because they want something.'

'But aren't there any people who are in between?' asked Michael.

'There are just a few who change their size according to who they're with. Some make them feel like giants; others make them feel as small as a dwarf. And there are a very very few people who always stay the same and look neither up nor down. They're strong enough to manage their own lives, so they don't expect other people to do things for them, and they won't let the bossy giants bully them. I call these rare people levellers.'

'But how can you tell if a person is a giant or a dwarf – or even a leveller – if it doesn't show on the outside?' asked Michael.

'You just sit in a corner and watch the way people talk to each another,' replied his father. 'The knack comes with practice.'

The prince thought for a while, then he looked sideways down the high table at his two favourite knights.

'Sir Roger must be a very big kind giant!' he said adoringly. He admired the dashing young knight only slightly less than his father!

'As a matter of fact, I think Sir Roger is a dwarf,' was his father's unexpected opinion. 'He is always looking up at giants because he wants their respect and approval because, astounding as it may sound, he feels very small indeed.'

Prince Michael obviously found that very hard to believe, so he said, 'And Sir Marmaduke?'

'Most of the time he's rather a bossy giant, but he can become the kind, caring sort sometimes,' smiled Paxalom.

'You're the kindest giant in the whole wide world,' yawned Michael happily, but Paxalom shook his head.

'I'm afraid kings can turn red and bossy very easily indeed. It's an occupational hazard for any kind of leader!'

This was far too much for Michael, particularly at that time of night. He yawned again as he asked, 'Will you choose levellers tomorrow?'

'I doubt it,' replied Paxalom. 'They don't make good leaders because they're either too good at seeing the other person's point of view or so self-contained they don't even *want* to see it. I guess I'll be looking for kind giants.'

'Father, what am I?' asked Michael poking sleepily at his jelly.

'It's too early to tell,' laughed his father. 'Children always have to start by being dwarfs, but the best grown-ups are levellers – provided they have the ability, on certain occasions, to become a kind giant or a humble dwarf.'

Paxalom turned to talk to the neglected guest on his right and when he looked back his son was fast asleep with his head pillowed on his jelly.

Many years later, when Michael himself became king, he always said that he had learned more about people during the day that followed than he had learned in years with his tutors and their dusty old books. Paxalom gave a garden party in the grounds of his royal residence, to which he invited everyone who was eligible to become one of the four new governors. As the king wove his way through the crowds Michael trotted along beside him, listening intently as his father talked to people about their interests, families and friends.

'It's always more important for a king to listen than to talk,' he told Michael as they sat in the shade, watching their guests from a distance and weighing up each one carefully. 'Now you tell me which are the four kind giants I should choose.'

'You must have had such an awful day, Your Highness,' said Sir Roger as he helped the young prince into bed that night. 'Fancy having to talk to all those boring people!'

'Oh no, it was gorgeous!' replied Michael. 'We've been hunting giants and dwarfs all day long!'

9

Castle Invincible

Before his downfall a man's heart is proud, but
humility comes before honour. (Proverbs 18:12)

'It isn't fair!' fumed Sir Roger, thumping the Octagonal
Table with his fist.

'I've been a Knight of the Octagonal Table for ten years
now, and the king still hasn't given me a decent assignment!'
The knights were waiting for the king to arrive for their
usual Monday morning council meeting, but his unusually
late arrival had given Sir Roger a chance to air his grievance.
Sir Marmaduke was not looking sympathetic.

'You're one of His Majesty's knights!' he said incredulously. 'Surely that's a big enough honour for anybody.'

'Yes, but I want to do something really important,' complained Sir Roger, 'make my mark before I'm too old.'

'But I've heard so much about all the battles you've
fought and the brave things you've done!' said the newest
knight, who still thought Sir Roger was wonderful.

'And I know who told you about them,' muttered Sir

Marmaduke, but Sir Roger did not hear him.

'That's just it,' he said, giving the young knight an encouraging smile. 'I've got an excellent record, but I'm always sent to fight under someone else's command. I'm never trusted to run my own show!'

'That's because you're still too bumptious!' said Sir Marmaduke sourly.

'You have to have self-confidence to get anywhere these days,' protested Sir Roger.

'King Paxalom's knights don't!' replied Sir Marmaduke. 'All they need is obedience.'

'But I do obey him,' shouted Sir Roger. And then, with a flush, he added more quietly, 'Well nearly always.'

'Exactly!' said his opponent with satisfaction. 'I think the reason you haven't been given a big assignment yet is because the king isn't quite sure if you trust him enough to obey his orders without question.'

'The only way he *could* be sure is by giving me the chance to prove it,' said Sir Roger crossly. Just then they heard the king's footsteps coming through the hall, so he raised his voice and added, 'I'm wasting my life and all my training hanging around here like this!'

'Pride will be your undoing,' muttered Sir Marmaduke, who always liked to have the last word.

A few weeks later, Sir Roger was surprised, and pleased, when Paxalom asked him to stay behind after the council meeting.

'I've been wondering if the time has come for you to be trusted with a major responsibility,' said the king, but he didn't look as pleased about the idea as Sir Roger.

On one wall of the council chamber was a huge map of the empire, and pointing to the top of it with a gigantic finger, Paxalom said, 'Trouble!'

The northern border of his territory lay next to a small and relatively unimportant kingdom, but it was ruled by a man who had always been his arch-enemy. For years this king had been sending raiding parties across the bordering mountains to steal sheep, cattle and even women on occasions.

'I've always left King Hector alone,' said Paxalom, 'but I've heard disturbing rumours lately that he plans to join forces with some of our other northern enemies. That could become very serious indeed if we don't take a firm stand quickly. I need someone to go up there, build a strong castle in a strategic spot, gather and train an army of local warriors and hold that entire border for me. Do you think you could strike terror into Hector's heart before he gets too many big ideas?'

'Oh yes, sire!' said Sir Roger ecstatically. 'I'd love to!' He felt positively dizzy. This was big: his own army, his very own castle, and right up against enemy lines! It was better than his wildest dreams – his chance to prove his worth to all those other knights. In a surge of gratitude he flung himself down on his knees before the king and kissed his hand.

'You'll be away for a very long time,' said Paxalom sadly. 'I shall miss you.'

Sir Roger felt touched. 'I shall miss you too, Your Majesty,' he said, and he meant it.

'Remember,' continued Paxalom, looking at him searchingly, 'never allow yourself to become too busy to write to me every day, and I shall reply instantly by special messenger. That way we won't lose touch with each other.'

'I shall ask your advice before making any decisions,' promised Sir Roger happily, 'and any orders you send me, I'll obey instantly!'

When the expedition was finally ready to set off, the king came down to the courtyard himself to offer Sir Roger the stirrup cup; but the king was looking utterly miserable.

'I'm aware that by giving you this important job I risk losing you for ever,' he said sadly.

'Oh, but I will be very careful,' promised Sir Roger confidently. But he had not understood what King Paxalom meant, and that was what worried the king most.

'Bumptious,' muttered Sir Marmaduke, watching from the battlements. 'Pride will be his undoing, mark my words.'

'That is where I'll build my castle!' exclaimed Sir Roger to his officers the day they finished their long journey north. At the far end of a grassy plain were the high, snow-capped mountains that marked the edge of King Paxalom's empire. At their foot, rising steeply from the plain, was a hill with a conveniently flat top. 'Yes,' smiled Sir Roger, 'a castle built there would dominate the whole area.'

Castle Invincible took two years to build. Masons had to be sent into the mountains to cut the great grey stones; woodcutters hacked down pine trees for the carpenters; hundreds of labourers dug out the moat and diverted mountain streams to provide a water supply; farms had to be established to feed the huge garrison, not to mention their wives and camp followers. So, long before the castle was finished, a shantytown of little wooden houses grew around the base of the hill.

Those first few years were hectically busy for Sir Roger, but he loved every minute of them. Not only did he have to organise the building of the castle and train his soldiers, but he found himself overseeing this whole new settlement. At first, the greatness of his task weighed heavily on him; he missed his king terribly and spent at least an hour every evening writing him long letters. The arrival of the special messenger bringing Paxalom's encouraging replies was always the best moment of Sir Roger's day. Should the messenger be late, he would climb onto the battlements and wait anxiously until he spotted the galloping horse in the far distance.

One of the first things he did was to infiltrate the enemy's domain on the far side of the mountains with an efficient spy ring. They never had anything sinister to report, so he had plenty of time to spend on expanding his castle until it was the largest in the world. It held so many soldiers that traders of all kinds were needed to support them, and soon the surrounding township sprawled over a wide area. Sir Roger found himself responsible for thousands of people who bowed low whenever they saw him, hung on his every word and called their sons Roger in his honour.

The more absorbed he became with building up his outpost, the less time there seemed to be to write to the king. Because Paxalom only replied when his knight communicated with him, the special messengers arrived much less frequently, but Sir Roger no longer waited for them on the battlements. The castle itself had become his pride and joy.

He would stand on its highest tower every morning and evening, and revel in its invincible strength.

'It's a pity those other Knights of the Octagonal Table can't see it,' he thought. The idea of having a picture painted of the castle and sent to King Paxalom for his birthday seemed like a good way of showing them all how well things were going. He could already imagine it hanging in the council chamber, where the other knights would have to look at it every Monday morning.

'Paint me standing in the foreground,' he told the artist. The poor young man made five attempts before Sir Roger was satisfied, and in the final version the knight himself was so big the castle could hardly be seen.

'But that was the way he wanted it,' shrugged the artist.

When the king's birthday present finally arrived, it was so big it took sixteen men to carry it over the drawbridge. Paxalom stood staring at it for a long time, but he did not look pleased. He had it put away in a barn and it finished up as a useful barrier between two pigsties.

'Come and stay with me, Roger,' wrote Paxalom that evening. 'I'm worried about you – we need to spend time together.'

Sir Roger wrote back saying he was highly honoured by the invitation, but this was not a good time to be away. 'Too much is happening here and who knows what they would all get up to if I left them to it?'

Sir Marmaduke shook his head sadly when the king showed him the letter. 'When a man thinks he is indispensable,' he said, 'he's definitely in danger.'

A castle of such lavish proportions required an astonishing

amount of maintenance and, as time went by, Sir Roger found himself tied up endlessly with plans for repairing the roof or decisions over new colour schemes for the state apartments. He also discovered that being the pinnacle of such a large people-pyramid meant he had to spend hours sorting out domestic problems or disputes between neighbours. However, the gratitude he received for his efforts made him feel so good he never minded how many hours he spent holding court.

'I work from morning 'til night,' he wrote, when the king next asked him to come home for a while. 'I start at five and never finish before midnight. How can you possibly expect me to fit anything more into this summer?'

Paxalom noticed the tinge of self-pity that had crept into his letter. 'He's close to burn-out,' he told Sir Marmaduke with a sigh.

By the time several key members of Sir Roger's spy ring had mysteriously disappeared, he was so overworked he didn't get round to replacing them, or even to discovering why they had vanished in the first place.

'What's the point?' he told himself. 'The enemy is never going to attack a man of my reputation, in such a well-defended castle.'

When traders from over the mountains told stories about a fiery young chieftain who had joined forces with King Hector and was claiming he would soon rule the world, Sir Roger merely shrugged and said to Basil, his second-in-command, 'All young men say that.'

'But sir,' persisted Basil, 'reports also say this puppy is training a large army.' But Sir Roger was too busy designing a garden in the castle keep to take any notice. He had now grown so fat his armour had to be enlarged, and few of his warhorses were strong enough to carry him.

When news came of imminent invasion, Basil suggested that they should let King Paxalom know they needed reinforcements. But Sir Roger flew into a rage. 'Certainly not!' he snapped. 'I can handle this.' He was proud of his army and he had always wanted to have the opportunity to show it off to the world. 'I don't want those other knights bringing their soldiers up here and getting all the glory. This i *my* castle.'

'But sir,' persisted Basil, who had always been noted for his bravery, 'isn't it actually the *king's* castle?'

Basil was instantly stripped of his rank, put on a charge for insubordination and sent home in deep disgrace.

It was during a banquet that Sir Roger was giving for the distinguished visitors who had come to admire his castle that the enemy eventually struck. They had been hiding in the mountains, and at the height of the celebrations a kitchen boy turned traitor let down the drawbridge for them. The castle that Sir Roger had thought was invincible was overrun in a matter of minutes. Everyone was killed everything valuable was stolen; and the town below the walls was burnt to the ground.

King Hector and his young ally were so delirious with triumph they put a notice on the castle gate. It read: 'I King Paxalom trusts such a fat fool to represent him, he must be an even bigger fool himself!'

They thought it was hilariously funny, and all their soldiers were laughing and celebrating so much that when King Paxalom and his army suddenly pounced on them they were quickly defeated. Basil had gone straight to the king on his return, and Paxalom had instantly mustered the army and set off to the rescue.

'Well, Your Majesty,' said the oldest Octagonal Knight, gazing up at the embarrassing notice, 'you're well rid of Sir Roger!'

For once Sir Marmaduke did not say anything – he was weeping too much to speak. King Paxalom also had tears in his eyes as he turned to the youngest knight and said, 'Go and see if you can find Sir Roger's body; then we can bury him with dignity.'

The young man was back almost at once. 'I've found him, on the battlements,' he said breathlessly. 'He must have been trying to keep control of the castle, right to the very end; but sire, I'm not quite sure, but I think he might not be . . . completely dead.'

Paxalom sprang up the stone stairs to the battlements three at a time and knelt beside the crumpled body of his favourite knight. It was many hours since Sir Roger had been fatally wounded, but he had willed himself to live. Perhaps he knew Paxalom would come? As his eyelids flickered and he looked up into the face of his king, he managed to say, 'I failed you.'

'It's all right,' replied the king. 'You won't next time. No knight is much use to me until he's failed and lost all his self-confidence. The broken ones put all their confidence in me.'

As he pulled the elixir from under his breastplate, Sir Roger shook his head.

'You want to die?' asked Paxalom sadly. 'It's your choice.' He could see Roger's life was ebbing away, but the knight was struggling to say something more.

'I can't be your knight . . . but let me be your servant . . . scrub floors . . . clean boots . . . but stay near you.'

King Paxalom was laughing as he put the miraculous drop into Sir Roger's mouth. 'My knights are my knights for ever!' he said. 'And they all have equal honour, whatever I ask them to do.'

As they all rode home in triumph, Sir Marmaduke kept close beside his old sparring partner all the way. He had missed Sir Roger far more than he cared to admit.

'The lad needs looking after,' he thought. 'He's too quiet; not like himself at all.'

But Sir Roger had many things on his mind. The future was far from clear, but he was perfectly certain that, from then on, he was not just going to obey the king '*nearly* always' any more!

10

The Guilty Secret

The punishment that brought us peace was upon him, and by his wounds we are healed. (Isaiah 53:5)

King Paxalom had a nephew, the only son of his sister. She had been fifteen when Paxalom was born and already married off to the austere ruler of a distant kingdom. It was many years before she presented her husband with an heir, and when their son finally arrived the birth was so difficult that the queen detested the child on sight.

'I shall call him Felix,' she said, 'because cats are much nicer than babies.'

His father merely said it was a pity the prince was so ugly. The baby prince was handed to a severe-looking nurse and banished to a distant wing of the palace.

Prince Felix was a very good quiet baby who grew into a very good quiet boy. He badly wanted his parents to love him, but his father was always too busy and his mother only loved her cat, which was large and white. When it sat on the queen's lap, its green eyes seemed to say to Felix, 'Go away – we don't want you.'

If the prince ever failed to be quiet and behave perfectly, his parents refused to speak to him or look at him for weeks on end. Their disapproval was so awful that he was never anything but perfectly behaved.

One morning, when Felix was eight, he woke to find the whole palace in an uproar. Wherever he went he fell over servants scrubbing and polishing in a positive frenzy of cleanliness. He was too nervous to ask anyone what was happening, so he just smiled, as he always did, and was extra quiet and good.

From the window of his schoolroom he watched a stream of carts rumbling over the castle drawbridge, laden with all kinds of food and wine. The king was so mean his household lived mostly on bread, water and gruel. Felix had never seen so much food in his life, so at last he dared to ask his grim-faced tutor, 'Please, sir, what is happening?'

The tutor looked flustered, like everyone else in the palace. 'Your uncle, King Paxalom, will be staying here tonight,' he replied with a note of awe in his usually harsh voice.

'My uncle must be a very greedy man,' said Felix looking back at all those loaded carts. 'Can he really eat that much – all in one go?'

'Stupid child!' snapped the tutor. 'He is the richest king in the world, so he travels with a vast entourage. You are to sit at the high table tonight for the state banquet, so you must be extremely good and not disgrace your father.'

Prince Felix, who was always extremely good and would

rather have died than disgrace his father, promised earnestly that he would be perfect. But as the day wore on all the noise in the palace brought on one of his sick headaches.

'You *can't* be sick!' said his mother furiously. 'I want you to make a good impression on your uncle.'

'You *won't* be sick!' thundered his father. But Felix was.

In terrible disgrace he was sent to bed and lay there in the dark listening to the heralds trumpeting their welcome fanfare.

'You *must* be better by now!' said his mother, on her way to the banqueting hall, but he wasn't. So the queen swept away in disgust, her precious cat under one arm.

Felix put a pillow over his head but he could still hear the clashing music and rumble of voices as the banquet began. There was laughter too. Felix had never heard anyone laugh before – his father disapproved of frivolity.

Suddenly he heard footsteps coming towards his room. Nervously he watched the door open and a man he had never seen before came in carrying a candle. His clothes were not grand enough for him to be one of the important guests, so Felix thought he must be one of his dreaded uncle's servants, come to drag him downstairs for a royal inspection. He smiled politely, just as he always did, and watched as the man lit several candles from the one he carried, and then sat down on the bed.

'That's more cheerful,' he remarked pleasantly. Felix smiled again. 'It's horrid being sick, isn't it?' continued the stranger. 'What's your record? I once managed seventeen times in one day.'

Felix's eyes were round with wonder. 'Your parents must have been terribly angry,' he whispered.

'Of course not! No one can help being sick. My grand-mother used to let me sit on her knee while she told me stories.'

Felix thought about the cat on his mother's lap and wished dolefully that he had a grandmother.

'It's terribly cold in here,' the man continued. 'What happened to your fire?'

'Oh, I never have one,' explained Felix. 'You see, princes have to learn to be tough if they are to grow up to be good kings.'

'Really?' said the visitor, looking interested. 'Do you ever play soldiers?'

'Play?' replied Felix blankly. His father had banned all toys, saying, 'Princes must work, not waste time'. But this man obviously didn't know much about princes because he produced two little wooden soldiers from his pocket. 'I used to have an army of them when I was boy,' he said, 'but only these two are left now.' Felix didn't know what to say, so he just smiled politely.

'I used to make them wonderful castles with my bed-clothes and pillows,' continued the man. 'Shall I show you?' A few minutes later the soldiers were guarding a cas-tle, complete with a moat and dungeons. For one glorious hour Felix managed to forget that he was a prince and found that he was rather good at playing. At last his visitor said, 'I guess it must be time for your mother to tell you a bedtime story?'

Felix smiled even more widely than usual. 'Oh no!' he said. 'Queens never have time to tell stories.'

'Do kings?'

'They're busier still!'

'Then I'll just have to tell you one myself,' laughed his visitor, and tucking Felix up snugly he began. 'Once upon a time . . .'

'Get up at once!' shouted Felix's tutor early next morning. He was standing over the bed, threateningly, while the gentlemen of the bedchamber hovered nervously in the background. 'Your uncle is leaving in half an hour and their majesties insist that you come downstairs immediately to wish him goodbye.'

'I'm . . . I'm going to be sick,' faltered Felix.

'It will be more than your life is worth if you're sick in the presence of King Paxalom,' said the tutor severely and pulled him out of bed.

Half an hour later, dressed in his very best clothes, stiff with fur and jewels, Felix was following his tutor downstairs with the awful words ringing in his ears: 'Don't you *dare* disgrace your father.'

He slid silently into the Great Hall where his parents were saying goodbye to their distinguished guests. They were too busy to see him at first, and he felt so shy his stomach began heaving ominously.

'There you are at last!' snapped the queen. 'Come here and bow to your uncle.' Felix bowed without waiting to be introduced, but when he finally straightened up he found himself gazing into the face of the man who had shown him how to play soldiers. His look of astonishment was so comical, King Paxalom burst out laughing. Then he crouched down so that his eyes were on a level with Felix's and he said, 'I'm so sorry, little nephew, I thought you knew who I was when I came to say goodnight to you.'

'I . . . I . . . didn't know . . . I had no idea kings ever . . . played.'

'This one does,' replied his uncle. 'I brought you a present,' he added, beckoning a servant, who came forward carrying a large wooden box. Presents were thought to be an unnecessary distraction for princes, so Felix had never been given one before, and he was not sure what to do.

'Say thank you, boy!' ordered his father, but Felix could say nothing as his uncle opened the wrappings and handed him a perfect model castle carved from wood.

'Look,' said Paxalom, 'the drawbridge lifts up like this; and if you open the keep you will find a whole garrison of soldiers waiting for your command.'

Felix was so pleased he even forgot to smile.

'Wretched, ungrateful boy!' boomed his father, and Felix just knew he was going to be sick. Forgetting that he must never turn his back on a king, he rushed from the room.

'He will be whipped for this!' said the king furiously.

'He was not ungrateful!', protested King Paxalom, looking at his brother-in-law in despair. 'He was too pleased to speak; he must not be punished for that!'

But he was. Later his father summoned him to his presence and said, 'Your uncle's present was most disappointing. We had hoped he would give you something useful. However, it can be used to teach you military strategy if it is displayed in your schoolroom. But remember your uncle will want to see it looking perfect when he next comes to see us, so you must never touch it.'

So Felix endured long boring lessons by gazing at his toy castle and remembering the man who had given it to him. In bed at night he imagined they were playing with it together.

'One day, I want to be just like my uncle,' he vowed. 'I hope he comes back soon.'

One terrible day his parents were both in such a bad mood that even his usual polite smile could not prevent their displeasure.

'Go to the schoolroom and write a thousand lines!' said his father grimly, when all he had done was sneeze. Miserably he made his way upstairs, telling himself that at least he could sit near his uncle's castle. But when he arrived he found his mother's obnoxious cat curled up on top of it.

'Go away,' its green eyes seemed to say. 'This is *my* castle now!'

The frustrations of Felix's day focused on the cat. 'Get off!' he shouted, but it arched its back and hissed at him from the wooden battlements. He made a grab at the cat, but in the scuffle the castle crashed to the floor and was broken into pieces.

'I hate you!' shouted Felix as he pelted the cat with the wreckage. The artful creature avoided them disdainfully and left Felix alone among the scattered ruins. Horror swept over him. No one would believe him if he said the cat had broken the castle. His father would blame him and be furious; and his uncle certainly wouldn't want to be his friend.

Then he had an idea. Once, when he had been locked in his bedroom without food all day, he had discovered he could move the floorboards under his bed; the cavity between the oak joists had become his secret hiding place for bits and pieces he was sure his parents would think were a waste of time. Quickly he gathered up the broken pieces of his toy and as many of the soldiers as he could find, and ran to his bedroom. When the castle was safely hidden he hurried back to the schoolroom, flung open the window and disarranged the cushions on the sill.

When his tutor came in Felix looked up from his books and smiled even more politely than usual and said, 'Sir, I think a thief must have come through the window and taken the model castle.'

The hue and cry began at once; the whole palace was searched and the king declared that the culprit would be executed. Felix was sick for days; his parents thought he was upset over the loss of his castle and were almost kind, but this only made him feel worse. Great waves of shame washed over him whenever he thought about the secret place under his bed. 'I'll never open it again,' he vowed. But he did!

For his next birthday he was given a bow and arrows. He was delighted at first, then he discovered that on top of his tight timetable of lessons and princely sports he now had to fit in an hour's archery practice every day.

'That's no good!' roared the king, when he came to check his son's progress.

'But sir, it was nearly a bull's-eye,' Felix protested tearfully.

'Princes don't *nearly* score bull's-eyes!' snapped his father. 'They win every time.'

One day, when Felix arrived early for his archery lesson, he noticed his mother's cat asleep under a cherry tree. 'I'll give it a fright,' he thought, and aimed an arrow at the trunk above the cat's head. The arrow flew too low, and with a last yowl of rage the cat was speared through the heart.

Felix gasped. What would his mother say? How could he

tell her? Any hope of winning her love was lost for ever. But suppose she didn't know who killed her cat?

Hastily he wrapped it in his cloak with the blood-stained arrow, and hurried off to his bedroom. Barring his way on the stairs was his tutor.

'Sir,' Felix said, 'I'm going to be sick.' With a snort of annoyance the tutor let him go and Felix only just had time to stow his grisly burden in the hiding place before the royal physicians arrived with their bottles of nasty medicine.

When her beloved cat could not be found, the queen gave way to such terrible grief that Felix felt the sound of her crying would haunt him all his life.

'I'll never be a king like Uncle Paxalom,' he thought wretchedly. 'I am a murderer now as well as a liar!' And from that time his smile lost its sweetness and stiffened into a mask.

Of course it was not long before the prince's bedroom began to smell very bad indeed.

'It's only the sewers,' said the king, when Felix's tutor broached the awkward subject. 'It'll toughen him up!' But it didn't. He was sick even more often than usual and even after the smell had gone the thought of it was enough to bring on one of his attacks.

A year later, when the queen produced a baby, she said it might even make up for the loss of her 'kitty', and she would sit with the baby on her lap, stroking him as she had once fondled her cat. The king actually smiled and said, 'Now at last I have a son of whom I can be proud!'

'I hate him!' thought Felix dismally. 'Even more than the cat!'

The new baby prince slept in the room next to Felix, attended by a bevy of nursemaids. One night, when most of them had gone down for their supper, the girl they had left to watch over the baby slipped out onto the battlements to see her sweetheart. She told herself she would certainly hear the baby if he cried. But she did not hear him choke as he lay there alone on his back.

Felix, who never seemed to be able to sleep any more, lay in his bed wondering if it was possible to kill a baby simply by hating him through a wall. Then he began to hate himself for thinking like that. He was cold and deeply lonely, and he thought about the nice warm fire that always burned in his brother's room. Perhaps the nursemaid might let him sit beside it for a while if he went and asked her for a drink. So he slid out of bed and went next door, only to find the nursemaid gone and the fire out. Crossing to the big wooden cradle he knew at once the baby was dead.

'I killed him,' he moaned, 'just as surely as I killed the cat! They'll know it was me.' In a blind panic he scooped the baby up and ran with him to his own room. The secret hole was opened in a moment and he was back in bed with his head under the pillow long before pandemonium broke out next door.

The servant girl and her lover were executed and a local witch was burned alive for spiriting the baby away by black magic.

'We are having a most annoying time,' wrote the queen to her illustrious brother. 'We've mislaid the baby and Felix is being even more awkward than usual; he refuses to eat, even when held down and forced by four strong men!'

'Coming at once!' wrote Paxalom in return. 'Leaving first thing in the morning.'

'Your brother? Coming here again!' protested the king. 'Just think of the expense!'

The queen merely sniffed, but Felix, standing in the shadows of the Great Hall, felt as if he were turning to ice. For ages he had longed for nothing more than a visit from his uncle, but now it was the last thing he wanted. 'I've turned into an evil monster since he was here,' he told himself sadly. 'I would never dare to look him in the face again.'

All through the night before his uncle's arrival he lay tossing, sleeplessly. After the baby's disappearance the nursery wing had been closed and Felix was given a new set of rooms. He had hoped it might be easier to sleep in a bed that did not cover such a ghastly secret – but it made no difference. Long before dawn he knew what he had to do. 'I'm not fit to be a prince,' he decided, 'so I can't stay here and go on pretending.'

The servants, working all night to prepare the welcome banquet, never noticed a thin little boy slip out through the postern gate; and the forest trees had hidden him completely, long before the sun rose.

If it had not been for a woodcutter who happened to recognise the prince, his father might well have burned yet another witch when his disappearance was discovered in the morning.

'How dare he run away and make us look fools in front of your brother!' fumed the king, who blamed the queen entirely. 'I've told the search parties to get him back here before Paxalom arrives – on pain of death!'

But unfortunately for the searchers Paxalom arrived early.

He strode into the Great Hall well before midday and gave his sister a present of two white kittens. She was so pleased she quite forgot to be worried about her son. The gift he presented to her husband was definitely less well received. A court jester was the very last thing he wanted!

'And where is that nephew of mine?' asked Paxalom looking around hopefully. 'I've brought him some more soldiers to add to his collection.' A deathly silence greeted his enquiry.

'He's ill,' said the queen vaguely.

'What have you done to him?' demanded Paxalom, who could tell something was desperately wrong.

'Oh, he's just a rather difficult child,' replied the queen, already absorbed in her cats. 'He's probably hiding some-where – he's so irritating!'

Her husband shot her a furious look, but she had pattered away in search of two saucers of cream. 'The wicked child will be severely whipped when he gets home,' he growled, but he failed to see that his brother-in-law was now white with rage.

Paxalom's knights had noticed, and they trembled! The king was terrifying when his fury was roused. Would he explode and start a major war, they wondered, as they surreptitiously felt for their swords.

Paxalom's voice was deceptively quiet as he said, 'Send the prince's tutor to fetch the blankets from his bed.'

'He's just been executed for negligence,' growled the king.

'I want the blanket from my nephew's bed,' replied Paxalom, and there was something in his tone that made his brother-in-law nod to a servant without another word.

'Put it down on the floor,' ordered Paxalom, when one

miserably thin blanket finally arrived. Striding to the hall door, he called the hunting dogs that accompanied him everywhere. When they had sniffed the blanket thoroughly, the brief command 'Find!' sent them off again, baying loudly. Without so much as a glance at his brother-in-law, Paxalom mounted his horse and rode away after them – followed by five of his trusted knights.

Felix began to feel frightened as soon as the forest trees closed in around him. He knew wolves prowled there, and trolls cast evil spells. 'Princes are never afraid of anything,' he had always been told, but that only proved he was a failure. When the sun rose, the day became very hot; his shoes pinched and he could feel a sick headache coming on. 'I can't ever go back,' he thought, 'but I'm too tired and frightened to go on.' When he finally reached the edge of a precipice, it seemed like the answer to all his problems. It would be so easy to let himself fall, fall, fall and never have to walk another step.

Paxalom rode through the forest just ahead of his dogs so he could call them off the moment he caught sight of the boy. He didn't want to terrify him by the sudden appearance of four huge dogs. In the end, however, he spotted Felix before the hounds saw him, and halted them with a single word. He could see the little boy, standing at the edge of the ravine, and knew at once that he was in awful danger.

'Felix, wait, I'm coming!' He had hoped to reassure the boy, but instead the sound of his voice was the spur that made him jump. His body was so light that it seemed to flutter down, bouncing and smashing on the jagged rocks until it finally lay still by the torrent that roared through the gorge.

It took Paxalom and his knights several hours to edge their way down to where he lay, his broken limbs sprawled in all directions. His uncle knelt beside him, and opening a small bottle he put one drop of dark red liquid on Felix's lips. Over the years the precious elixir in the bottle had been refilled time and time again by the blood, sweat and tears Paxalom had shed for his people.

The five knights clustered around them and gasped in wonder as the child's eyelids fluttered, colour seeped back into his face and the broken bones straightened themselves and fitted back together.

'Uncle,' he muttered, and fell asleep.

'He'll do,' smiled Paxalom. It took them twice as long to climb back up again, but the king insisted on carrying his nephew himself, and even when he rode back through the forest he still cradled the child in his arms.

They were not far from the palace when Felix woke and looked up anxiously into his uncle's face. 'Sir, you're not going to take me home, are you?' he whispered with a shudder. Paxalom reigned in his horse and motioned his knights to move away.

'Why not?' he asked tenderly.

'I can't be a prince any longer,' whispered the boy. 'I am too wicked.'

'Tell me,' said his uncle softly.

'I lied when the cat broke your lovely castle. I killed it by mistake with one of my arrows, but I never owned up and then . . . then . . . ' His sobs choked him, but his uncle seemed to be waiting. 'I killed my brother.'

'How?' asked Paxalom impassively.

'I hated him through his bedroom wall, and when I went in to look, he was dead.'

With a quick sigh of relief Paxalom smiled. 'Feelings alone aren't enough to kill someone,' he said gently. 'Babies do suddenly die in their cots sometimes. Are you quite sure you didn't do anything to harm him?' The enormous look of relief that was spreading over his nephew's face was all the answer Paxalom needed.

'I was so afraid I'd killed him,' said Felix, 'I hid him – with the cat.'

Paxalom had to blink away his tears before he said, 'You poor child; what you must have suffered – and all so unnecessarily. If only you had left the baby where he lay, no one would have blamed you.'

'But are you *really* sure hating, on its own, can't kill?' asked Felix anxiously.

'Quite sure,' replied Paxalom. Then he added gravely, 'But hatred in the heart is just as bad as murder – even if it hasn't the power to kill.'

'Then I ought to have died!'

'But you did die,' said Paxalom. 'The Felix who lied, deceived and hated died in the ravine. He is gone for ever. But I have given you a new life; you can be an entirely new Felix and start all over again. I came here today to suggest to your parents that you should come back and live with me for a while, as a son to me and a brother to my children. Would you like that?'

'Oh yes,' sighed Felix. 'And will you teach me to be like you? I've always wanted that.'

His uncle looked down at him quizzically. 'Are you *sure*?'

he asked. 'My standards of honesty are very high. If you want to be like me, you will have to tell your father and mother about your secret hiding place and what you have hidden in there.'

A look of pure terror crossed Felix's face.

'I shall tell them that the baby's death was not your fault,' continued Paxalom, 'but you will never be free of all that guilt and shame until you have confessed the things you did do wrong.'

'But sir, they will punish me . . . horribly.'

'But you deserve it,' said Paxalom very gravely. 'If punishment does not follow crime, then there is no justice.'

Felix clung desperately to his uncle's shirt. 'No!' he pleaded. 'I'm too afraid.'

'You will go on carrying that other Felix's shame until the punishment has been given. I want to see you free of shame.'

Felix was stiff with fear when they finally reached the castle. His parents and their entire household were waiting in the Great Hall. The queen sat with her kittens on her lap while the king paced up and down like a wolf in a trap.

'That boy!' he snarled at intervals. 'When he gets back I'll beat him to jelly.'

No one ran to welcome Felix when Paxalom carried him through the door.

'Our food is cold!' growled his father. 'The banquet is ruined.'

Paxalom put Felix down and gave him an encouraging push in the direction of his furious parent. 'Do it now and be free of it,' he whispered.

There was no way Felix could walk across the expanse of polished flagstones without his uncle's hand to hold, but together they managed it in the end.

'Father, Mother,' began Felix and gulped. 'I have done some terrible things . . .' The story came very slowly and the effect it had on the king and queen was dramatic. Even with clarification from Paxalom over the episode of the baby, they were outraged.

'You lied!' accused his father.

'You killed my kitty,' screamed his mother, 'and for all I know you killed my baby too!'

'You're going to pay dearly for all this!' finished his father. 'Sergeant! Fetch a whip and give him twenty lashes.'

Poor Felix was so horrified he fainted.

'And now I suppose you're going to ask me to let him off!' said the infuriated monarch, glaring at Paxalom.

'No! Punishment there must be. Twenty lashes will probably kill such a frail child, but you are the ones he has wronged, so you have a right to choose his punishment.'

The sergeant returned carrying a vicious whip, but Paxalom had not finished. 'Brother-in-law, do you remember the day we first met? You came to me because you were in debt. I paid it for you – do you remember?'

His brother grunted in recognition of the memory.

'Debts can be borne by someone else,' Paxalom continued, 'and so can punishments. Will you allow me to take Felix's punishment for him?' There was a startled silence.

'Surely,' said the queen acidly, 'such a great king would not take the punishment deserved by a nasty, wicked little boy?'

'Yes, he would,' replied Paxalom, 'if he loved that boy enough.'

'Let's forget the whole thing,' muttered Felix's father testily. 'If I let my sergeant loose on you, that would be the end of our trade agreement!'

'It would certainly be the end of it if you did *not* let him loose on me,' said Paxalom grimly. 'Nor must he be allowed to lighten his hand.'

Felix had come round from his faint by this time, and was struggling to his feet in horror as he realised what was about to happen.

'No! No! Uncle, I don't want them to hurt *you*!' he sobbed.

Paxalom's stern face relaxed as he smiled fondly at his nephew. 'But I want to do this because living without you would be far more painful for me than taking your punishment! Come on, Sergeant,' he said, stripping off his shirt. 'Get on with it, man.'

A few days later, when the shameful hiding place had been opened and its contents laid to rest, King Paxalom and his entourage set off for home, taking Prince Felix with them. His parents were so glad to be rid of him they hardly bothered to say goodbye.

It was early summer and the world beyond the forest looked fresh and green. 'Let's leave the old Felix behind in that ravine for ever, shall we?' smiled Paxalom. 'There's a new life ahead, ready for us to enjoy!'

11

The Sorry Tale of Baron Sebastian

Who will bring any charge against those whom God has chosen? It is God who justifies. Who is he that condemns? (Romans 8:33–34)

King Paxalom sat at his huge state desk, working carefully through piles of neatly stacked papers and letters. Out in the garden, beyond his windows, he could hear the sound of children playing. He smiled as he saw Michael and Felix galloping into view, riding broom handles into an imaginary battle. He had played just the same game in that very spot himself.

'Oh to be a child again!' he sighed and went back to his papers. The first letter he picked up was from the governor of the furthest province of his empire, more than two thousand miles away.

'Your Majesty will be concerned to know that your friend, Baron Sebastian, is in terrible trouble . . .' King Paxalom suddenly felt weak and had to ring for water before he could read more. Whatever could have happened to his old friend Seb?

When Paxalom had first arrived at the palace as a small child, just after losing both his parents, his grandfather had said, 'It is not good for you to grow up alone, Paxalom. I will find two pages to be your companions, sons of men I trust, and the three of you will be brought up together as brothers and treated exactly the same. You must never be allowed to think you are more special than other people, simply because you are a prince.'

So Sebastian and Philip had arrived, and what a good life the three of them had enjoyed together! They shared lessons, games – and punishments!

'We were more than friends and brothers; we were like triplets,' thought Paxalom as he sipped his water.

Growing up and having to part had been hard for them all. Philip became a soldier and died in battle, and Sebastian's father had died when he was only eighteen, forcing him to return home and run their vast estates.

'Don't be away long,' Paxalom had told him. 'I need you here at court.'

But Sebastian had never returned. At first, he wrote long letters full of the carefree fun he was having: glittering balls, girlfriends vying for his affection, fast horses and fashion-setting clothes. But after a time the letters had grown shorter and more infrequent, until they stopped altogether.

As Paxalom sat there, allowing the half-forgotten memories of Sebastian to flood through his mind, his face twisted with pain. The worst wound he had ever suffered had not been inflicted in battle by a lance or sword, but by his closest friend. For years he had tried to pretend it was not there, but now it completely engulfed him.

'How could Seb do that to me?' he whispered. 'Exclude me from his life as if our friendship had never existed.'

For months he had continued to write to Sebastian, asking him to come back for hunting trips, voyages, Christmas festivities, but his letters were always ignored.

Sometimes Paxalom had astonished himself by his own rage. 'I'm his king!' he would fume. 'I could *force* him to come and see me!' But when the anger had ebbed away he had known it was useless. 'Love is only real if it's given willingly,' he had told himself. 'He just doesn't want me or my friendship any more.'

The pain of rejection had been so acute that even now, so many years later, he knew the wound had still not fully healed.

'Is Your Majesty feeling ill?' asked the Lord Chamberlain anxiously.

Paxalom forced himself to smile. 'Thank you, I am better now,' he said, and picking up the governor's letter he read on.

'It pains me to tell Your Majesty that Baron Sebastian has lived a reckless, extravagant and, dare I say, wild life. He has wantonly spent all his father's wealth, neglected his estates and allowed his farm people to starve. I have often felt I should tell Your Majesty, but knowing of your friendship with the baron I felt it might be impertinent.'

'Pompous old fool!' muttered King Paxalom furiously, and then felt ashamed of himself for venting his pain on an innocent old man who was only doing his duty.

'However,' continued the governor, 'events are now in a state of crisis because Baron Sebastian has mortgaged his castle and borrowed such vast sums of money from his neighbour, Count Miser, that in two months' time everything he has will become the property of the said count who, as Your Majesty knows, is one of the most unpleasant subjects in your kingdom. I am sorry to bring Your Majesty such bad news, but I felt you should know.'

Paxalom allowed the letter to drop onto the desk, and there were tears in his eyes as he looked out across the garden where he and Seb had played, the lake where they had learned to swim and the hills where they had hunted together. 'You may be able to switch off your love for me,' he whispered, 'but I could never stop loving you, my oldest and closest friend.'

'I must go on a long journey,' he told the startled Lord Chamberlain. 'Baron Sebastian needs my help urgently.'

After many weeks of hard riding, King Paxalom and his knights arrived at their destination. A desolate sight awaited them. Buildings were falling down, farm animals were diseased and the roads were impassable. But it was the plight of the people that distressed Paxalom most.

'Nowhere else in this empire are my subjects treated like this!' he thundered as he looked at the starving, ragged figures who peeped nervously from dilapidated hovels. He saw nothing but disease and despair at every turn and children dying in their mothers' arms.

When they finally reached the castle itself it looked as shabby and neglected as all the other buildings, and as they rode into the main courtyard the slovenly servant hardly bothered to acknowledge their arrival.

King Paxalom dismounted and marched unannounced

into the Great Hall. The once stately room was reduced to a squalid mess; the roof had partly fallen in and chickens nested on the furniture. Lolling in a chair, surrounded by empty bottles and dirty tankards, was Sebastian – fast asleep. He had neither shaved nor washed for days and he was still wearing his nightshirt.

King Paxalom strode across the room in a terrible fury and glared down at him so ferociously that the knights clustered behind him were sure he was about to kill the baron with one terrible blow from his sword.

But as the king gazed down at the face he loved so well all his anger ebbed away, and he bent to kiss the matted shock of hair. Sebastian stirred, opened his eyes and gasped with pure joy. 'Paxalom! Oh how lovely . . .' Then a look of horror rapidly chased away the joy as he remembered himself and slid to his knees. 'Your Majesty,' he muttered and began to tremble violently, 'I'm sorry. I wasn't prepared for this great honour . . .'

'Seb,' said Paxalom softly, and taking his friend in his arms he held him while the baron sobbed his grief and shame over the king's enormous shoulder. Paxalom never interrupted, showed any condemnation or asked one reproachful question.

'I owe Count Miser more than all my lands and possessions are worth and he will take them all next week – and me as well. I deserve to be his slave, but my people don't; they fear and hate him even more than they loathe me. Oh, if only I could have my life over again!'

'You can, Seb! That's why I'm here. I came to pay off all your debt and to give you a fresh start, but first I'd be most grateful if you would go and have a bath and tell your servant to fetch me a good long drink!'

Before King Paxalom left for home he had paid off Baron Miser in full, and heaped upon Sebastian so much extra wealth that he had more than enough to repair every building and road on his lands, not to mention feeding and clothing his peasants for years to come.

As the two old friends shared a final stirrup cup, Paxalom said, 'Seb, remember I never want you or your people to lack anything, so if you need more money, promise you will tell me?'

'Sire, you have given me too much already.'

'Too much?' quizzed Paxalom. 'It isn't possible to give too much to someone you love.' Then he took Sebastian into his arms and added, 'Be happy, my dear old friend. Forget all that has happened; it is over and forgotten. Live in the present, marry a nice girl and enjoy your family! And don't forget to write.' With that he rode away, leaving Sebastian gazing gratefully after him.

And the baron did write. His letters were always full of love and praise for his king, and all the good things he was able to give and do for his people – now that he had the money.

'He seems to be working from dawn to dusk to make his peasants happy,' Paxalom told Sir Marmaduke, 'but he doesn't tell me if he's happy himself, and that bothers me.'

Some years later the king had to make a state visit to his most distant province, and while he was there he decided to pay Baron Sebastian a surprise visit. What a difference! The farms and villages looked prosperous and the people warm and well fed, but as the royal cavalcade swept up to the castle a terrible sight met their eyes. It was empty and derelict – an utter ruin.

'Where is your baron?' shouted the king to a little man fishing in the remains of the moat.

'He lives in the forest, sir, at the end of that path,' replied the man.

'Stay here,' the king ordered his knights. 'I will walk on alone.'

At the end of the path, hidden among dark trees and wedged beneath a towering black rock, he found a miserable hovel. No one seemed to be about so he walked inside. It was bitterly cold and damp and contained only a bare table, a chair and a small, hard bed. No fire had been lit in the hearth for a long time, and an atmosphere of harsh poverty hung over the place like a cloud.

Just then a figure shuffled through the back door, struggling with a heavy bucket of water. The hut was so dark he did not see the king standing in the shadows, but the king saw him only too clearly. Sebastian was dressed in rags, his feet were bare and covered in sores, and he was so emaciated his face looked like a skull.

He had begun to scrub some roots he had gathered for his meal when Paxalom's voice startled him.

'Why do you live here and not in your castle?' The king was shaking with passion.

'Paxalom!' gasped Sebastian. 'I didn't know . . . didn't see you . . .'

'I gave you the money to make your castle beautiful again. So why do you live in this hovel?' repeated Paxalom in an ominously quiet voice.

'I didn't want to spend any of your money on . . . on

myself,' stammered Sebastian miserably. 'I didn't feel I deserved to be happy after failing so badly. But I'm working hard to pay you back, although of course I could never hope to . . .' His voice trailed away because he could see how angry the king was looking.

'How dare you!' thundered Paxalom. 'Do you think it makes me happy to see you starving like a miserable pauper when I gave you enough to live like a prince? I wanted to share with you all that I have so you could live life to the full. Are you too proud to accept my love? This time you have hurt me quite unbearably!'

Sebastian sank to the floor and lay there huddled on the cold stones, but his king had not finished with him. 'How dare you condemn and cruelly punish a man I pardoned and wished to honour!'

'Sire,' protested Sebastian, 'I have never done that to anyone!'

'Except yourself! By forcing yourself to live like this you are torturing someone I happen to love, that infuriates me!'

'Majesty, I thought it would please you if I tried to pay back at least a little . . .'

'I didn't want repayment!' roared the king. 'I wanted your happiness!'

'Only tell me what I can do to please Your Majesty,' muttered Sebastian.

'You don't have to *do* anything,' replied Paxalom, pulling him to his feet. 'You're my friend. Come! We'll appoint a trustworthy steward to rebuild your castle and manage your estates, but you will come home with me so nothing can ever separate us again.'

So it was that Baron Sebastian lived at court for the last

few months of his life. His health never recovered and he seemed to have no desire to live. He spent his time lying with his face to the wall, refusing all the dainty food Paxalom sent up to his room. The king tried everything to lift Sebastian's spirits and he spent hours sitting by his bed retelling the stories of their boyhood adventures, but Sebastian would only sigh and say, 'Since those dear old days I've let you down so badly, Paxalom – I'm so sorry.'

One evening even the king's famous patience finally snapped, 'Why do you keep on saying you're sorry? You only had to say it once. I heard you the first time and forgave you instantly, so why can't you accept my forgiveness?'

'No one has ever disappointed you as much as I have,' said Sebastian. 'I just don't deserve your love or forgiveness.'

'But that is for me to decide. All you have to do is accept all I long to give you.' Paxalom stopped, blinking away his tears. 'Seb,' he continued in a gentler voice, 'can't you see you're breaking my heart? We could have years of living still ahead of us – hunting trips, adventures, music, laughter. Why do you refuse the life I'm offering you? Live, Seb, and make me happy! It would only take one drop of my elixir to heal you completely!' But Sebastian shook his head and turned his face to the wall so he could no longer see the expression on Paxalom's face.

When Baron Sebastian died, the king stood for a long time by his grave. Then, leaning heavily on Sir Roger's arm, he said softly, 'Sometimes I think love makes life so difficult. The more you love someone the more they're able to hurt you.'

'True, sire,' said Sir Roger thoughtfully. 'But while love may cause the worst kind of pain, doesn't loving, and being loved in return, also bring us the greatest joy life holds?'

Paxalom suddenly smiled. 'Sir Roger,' he said, 'that is quite the most sensible remark I have ever heard you make!'

12

The Land of Disguises

Woe to you, teachers of the law and Pharisees, you hypocrites! You are like whitewashed tombs, which look beautiful on the outside but on the inside are full of dead men's bones and everything unclean. (Matthew 23:27)

King Paxalom had a headache, and the noise his knights made as they took their places round the Octagonal Table that Monday morning thoroughly irritated him. As the squeaking, rattling and clanking of their armour finally subsided, he looked round at them all and said, 'I decree that in future suits of armour will be worn only in battle. The rest of the time knights will dress like everyone else.'

There was a deathly silence, then the protests began.

'Sire, no one would know who we were without it.'

'We wouldn't feel safe.'

'I'd feel naked.'

'If we wore ordinary clothes, people might think we were ordinary people.'

155

'Our armour is who we are!'

When the king finally held up his hand for silence, he was smiling in spite of his headache. 'Gentlemen,' he said, 'surely you know that you are not merely lumps of mobile metal? But as you seem so afraid to show the world who you *really* are, I withdraw my decree.'

With profound sighs of relief the Knights of the Octagonal Table settled down to the morning's business.

The following Monday, when they all clanked into their places, a visitor was shown into the council chamber. He was obviously a sailor, so they despised him on sight; and when they saw that his rank was low and his uniform scruffy, they knew he was quite beneath their notice. It irritated them not a little, therefore, to see how much respect King Paxalom seemed to give this visitor.

'Sam, would you be so kind as to tell these gentlemen your story?' he said, putting a kindly hand on the man's shoulder. And so the man began.

Well, Your Majesty – and gentlemen. I was sailing under Captain Blunt when a hurricane blew our ship so far off course that we had no idea where we were. Then we hit a rock and the ship went down with all hands – except mine, of course. I grabbed a plank and finally drifted ashore in a land I still can't seem to find on any map. I climbed a cliff in search of food and found myself on a track, which I hoped might lead to a farm or even a village. I was hungry by that time, I can tell you!

Round the corner, at just that moment, came a man dressed from head to foot in hedgehog skins. The prickles stood out really viciously in all directions.

'Please sir,' I said *very* politely, 'do you know where I could get something to eat?' But all he did was barge up to me so violently that his sharp prickles drove right through my shirt.

'Go away,' he said. 'Don't bother me.'

'Charming man,' I thought, hoping all the people in this land weren't pretending to be hedgehogs.

Just then I heard sobbing coming from behind a boulder by the roadside. Hurrying over, I saw a beautiful girl. Well, I guessed she must be beautiful but she was completely covered in silky scarves. She even had one round her face, so all I could see were two great big blue eyes looking at me appealingly.

'Oh, I'm so tired,' she said, 'and I'm lost. Please help me to get home.'

Helping damsels in distress is what you knights usually do, I know, but we sailors enjoy it too – whenever we get the chance! So I picked her up in my arms and carried her off down the track.

'Oh, thank you,' she kept whispering in my ear. 'How wonderfully strong you are!' She told me all about herself: said she was alone in the world, her parents were dead and the man she loved had just deserted her. Nearly had me crying, she did, until I suddenly saw this huge man crashing through the trees, heading straight for me. He must have been at least nine feet tall, and you never saw such well-developed muscles! Out he jumped, right in the middle of the track in front of us.

'Put her down – she's mine!' he yelled and up came fists the size of watermelons.

'Oh, there you are, darling,' says she, and without a

word of thanks she slips out of my arms. 'So much for all her "no one else in the world" stuff,' I thought, but I didn't have time to say anything before he had me pinned against a wall. I thought my time had come, I can tell you. Then, to my amazement, I saw a pair of eyes looking at me from two neat holes cut in his hairy chest. I gave his torso a cautious poke and discovered it wasn't real! He was just an ordinary-sized man hiding inside a huge blown-up disguise. I gave him a scornful kick in the midriff and he fell flat on his back.

'Time we were getting home, dear,' said he from deep inside the disguise, and the girl took his hand, and off they went. 'Extraordinary!' I thought. 'Perhaps it's some kind of national holiday here and they're all wearing fancy dress.'

I tried to walk on down the track, but by then I was so weak with hunger I collapsed by the roadside.

'Don't worry! I'm here. Let me help. I'll look after you.' I could hear this friendly voice, but all I could see was a huge round ball bouncing down the road towards me.

'You poor thing, you look exhausted,' it said. As it bounced nearer I could see the ball had feet and arms too, and a massive smile painted on one side. 'You need looking after,' it panted. 'My name's Friendly, by the way.'

As he shook hands with me I could see that painted all over the surface of the ball were things like, 'I'll help you' or 'Let me sort that out for you' and 'I can fix it'. I was beginning to wonder if the shipwreck had driven me mad!

'I live very near here,' he said. 'Quick, come back to my house; you really can't go round naked like that here, you know.'

Now let me tell you, I was wearing breeches and a shirt;

they were torn and grubby, but I certainly wasn't naked. So I told him I didn't think much of his rude remarks.

He apologised profusely. 'What I meant was, you're not wearing a disguise.'

'You mean the fancy dress outfits?' I said.

'Of course. We all wear them here. When we're children we decide what kind we want.'

'But why? What's wrong with breeches and a shirt?'

He dropped his voice to a whisper and hissed, 'You don't want people to know what you look like . . . underneath.'

'Why would that matter?' I asked.

'They might not like you . . . if . . . if . . . they saw what you were really like.' He was shuddering with embarrassment by this time. 'Surely that would worry you?'

'No,' I said blankly, 'why should it?' But I was beginning to understand. 'That first man I met, with all the prickles – is that the suit he wears, always?'

'Oh yes,' replied Friendly. 'He's got a heart of gold inside all that; he just doesn't want anyone to know it, that's all.'

'And the blown-up muscle-man?'

'Poor chap, he's always been a puny little weed; always bullied at school, so he chose to wear that suit. Very effective, isn't it?'

'Well, it certainly scared me – for a while anyway,' I said. 'And his girlfriend?'

'Wife, actually.' The ball bounced all over the road with amusement. 'She always seems to need someone to do things for her, so she droops about until people are so sorry for her they'll do anything she asks.'

'She's very good at it,' I agreed. 'Took me right in, I can tell you.' I wanted to ask why Friendly wore his 'let me help you' suit, but just at that moment I was nearly startled out of my breeches by a harsh shout from the rocks above.

'Attention!' Looking down at us was a soldier in full battledress, immaculate from his polished boots to his shiny brass helmet, but where there should have been rows of military medals there were words embroidered on his tunic: 'I'm in control', 'I expect instant obedience', 'I'm always right'. I didn't much like the look of the weapons he carried, I can tell you!

'Who are you and what exactly are you doing here?' he shouted at me.

'Oh hello, General,' said Friendly nervously. 'Nice to see you!'

The soldier ignored him but he pointed his sword at me in a most threatening manner.

'My ship was wrecked,' I explained.

'Why didn't you report to me, *instantly,* on your arrival?'

'I didn't know I was supposed to,' I said, trying my best not to sound scared.

'I'm looking after him, General,' said Friendly. 'Leave him to me. I'll fix him up with a disguise by tomorrow.'

'How dare you poke your nose into official business!' roared the General, and, leaping off the rocks, he whacked Friendly with the blunt end of his spear. A blow as heavy as that would have knocked most people unconscious but the ball just bounced up again, laughing.

'Hit away,' he giggled. 'No one can ever hurt me!'

'One of these days I'll find a way,' growled the General.

'You'd better be nice,' interrupted the Ball. 'Your wife's coming down the road looking for you.' Then he hastily turned to me and hissed, 'Don't touch her or you'll get stuck.'

I was just going to say that I had no intention of touching *anything* that belonged to that bully when I realised what Friendly had meant. The General's wife was completely covered in sticky pink spun sugar, and her wig was made of syrup.

'Oh, how lovely to meet you,' she gushed, holding out her sticky hands to me. 'You're so welcome.' I put my hands firmly behind my back and bowed instead. 'How *sweet* of you to come,' she said. 'You *must* come round for supper tomorrow. Friendly, you simply *must* bring him.'

'And I'll expect you to be wearing a proper suit,' barked the General, as he led his wife away. I could hear her sickly voice saying what a '*perfect sweetie*' I was.

'Poor dear,' sighed Friendly, 'she had such awful parents. Told her she was no good, useless, all that kind of thing, so she dressed herself up in all that sickly sweet sugar because she thought people would like her if she was always nice and sweet. She really believes the only way she'll make friends is by getting people stuck to her – permanently. Isn't it sad? She's so lonely because, of course, everyone's so scared of being trapped they keep well away from her.'

'And her husband?' I asked. 'Is he really a soldier?'

'No, but he was always a bully at school; used to make our lives a misery in the playground, and we all knew what kind of suit he'd wear when he grew up. He's not a real general – he just acts like one because he likes to be in control and tell everyone else what to do. Come on, my house is not far now.'

We were just turning a corner when a flashy sports chariot whizzed past, showering us with mud.

'Take no notice,' said Friendly, bouncing out of the

ditch where he had been thrown. 'That's only Bert – his vehicle is his suit! No one ever sees him without it. Makes him feel big and powerful. Other people here wear houses as their disguises. Take that one, for instance.'

He pointed to a magnificent mansion on the hillside nearby. 'Beautiful, isn't it? It's just Bill's disguise. He decided when he was a child that he could only feel a "somebody" if he had masses of money and piles of possessions. He's got that now but no one likes him. He must be so lonely rattling around all alone in that great place.'

'You're all mad round here!' I said. I wished I'd never set foot in the place, I can tell you. I was highly relieved when I saw a very ordinary-looking boy striding along the road in shirt and trousers.

'Well,' I said, 'at least there's one person not wearing a fancy suit!'

'But she *is*,' laughed Friendly. 'Underneath that masculine gear is a very pretty girl, but her parents wanted a boy, so she dresses up like that to please them and even chops off her lovely curls!'

A clown turning cartwheels down the middle of the road soon followed her.

'Don't tell me,' I said. 'That jester thinks that if he can make everyone laugh all the time, they won't realise how boring he really is!'

'My!' exclaimed the ball, looking most impressed. 'You *are* learning fast.'

Then he stopped so suddenly I bounced off him and fell in the mud.

'Don't worry, I'll help you. Are you hurt? Let me . . .'

'Stop fussing all the time,' I told him crossly.

'But I have to rescue everyone,' he said, looking as if he were going to cry. 'I *need* to look after people. I was just going to ask you if you could hear that bell. I'm sure you must be starving.'

I looked where he was pointing and there was the largest woman I ever saw coming round the corner. She was covered with bulging fat that quivered like a jelly as she walked, and her stomach stuck out so far it made a useful shelf for the tray she carried. I licked my lips when I saw how high it was piled with her home-baked cakes.

'Buns, doughnuts, pies for sale,' she was shouting as she rang her bell.

'She's the very best cook in the length and breadth of the land,' said Friendly very loudly, so she was bound to hear.

My mouth was watering, I can tell you, but just at that moment what looked like a clockwork mouse dashed out of a side road. He ran round and round the pie-seller in ever-decreasing circles. I could see the key sticking out of its side and it had a large label tied to it: 'I'm terribly busy . . . must keep going . . . mustn't relax.'

'Exhausting suit that!' snorted the ball as the clockwork mouse helped himself to a custard tart and whizzed away, squeaking, 'Can't stop, no time to waste.'

'He thinks he looks important, dashing around like that, but he's going to burn his motor out one of these days.'

'He never paid for his pie,' I said.

'Oh, she doesn't charge. She cooks for people because she wants to be needed.'

I was so hungry by that time I didn't care why she did anything, but yet another customer pushed in before I could help myself: he was wearing a suit that looked like a hard granite tower with legs sticking out of the bottom. It took the cook a maddeningly long time to push his buns and pies through the arrow slits in his thick grey walls.

'He was badly hurt once, poor chap,' whispered Friendly. 'He's determined never to be hurt again, so that's why he hides from everyone behind his defending walls.' This know-it-all ball was beginning to irritate me, so I said: 'How come you know so much about everyone else?'

'Oh, didn't I tell you? I'm a counsellor.'

'All right then,' I snorted, 'so why did the cook choose her suit?'

'She hates men,' he explained in a confidential whisper. 'Afraid of getting married.'

'I'd marry a cook like this any day,' I told him when I'd finished my tenth cake. Oh, they were good, I can tell you!

When we finally reached Friendly's house, I crashed out on the sofa and snored away 'til morning, but I was woken violently by him shouting in my ear.

'Hurry up! The General's called a council meeting to decide on your case. You must come to the market square immediately.'

'But I need a shave,' I protested, 'and a wash wouldn't go amiss.'

'Don't worry about that,' soothed Friendly. 'Once they've decided what suit to give you, it'll cover up everything. Wrap yourself in this sheet in the meantime.'

'No!' I said, pushing him away so hard he nearly bounced out of the window. 'I'll go as myself or not at all.'

'Oh dear, oh dear,' the ball kept saying reproachfully. 'You've got a real problem, haven't you?'

'*I've* got a problem?' I exclaimed as he dragged me through the streets.

When we arrived in the market square it was thronged with all kinds of extraordinary looking people. I stood gazing with my mouth open. You never saw a sight like that in your lives! In one corner there was a whole squad of athletes – fitness fanatics they were, all running on the spot or doing vigorous press-ups. Then a woman walked by, carrying several babies in her arms and dragging a load of older children along behind by her apron strings.

'She always hides behind her children,' whispered Friendly, who still seemed to feel the need to look after me all the time. There were quite a number of people who'd wrapped themselves up in thorns and brambles or even porcupine quills, and I gave them a very wide berth! At the back of the crowd I kept seeing what I took to be ghosts hovering about in the shadows. They unnerved me, so I gave Friendly a poke.

'What are those white blobs of mist? Spirits of the long departed?'

He bounced up and down with laughter. 'They're only shy people! The kind who prefer to be loners and stay on the edge of things; they'd rather watch from the sidelines than have to talk and make relationships. They're quite happy hiding in the mist and drifting about by themselves.'

At that moment a long line of stretchers arrived, and soon rows of patients were laid out down one side of the square.

'My! This land must be unhealthy,' I said.

I might have known old know-all would have the answer.

'They're not *really* ill,' he said cheerfully. 'They just decided to make their health (or lack of it) their suits; but they bring great happiness to the ones who like to dress up in medical uniforms and look after people.'

'You're all crazy!' I told him, but just then a hush fell on the whole gathering as the General himself marched into the centre of the square. Beside him walked a man in a striped suit; he wore a crinkly grey wig and clutched a writing tablet and several quill pens. I could see that the stripes in his suit were made from the words 'I am the expert', 'I'm important', 'I know what to do', 'I'm always right'. He made me feel small just looking at him, but I felt smaller still when the General pointed his lance at me and bellowed: 'We are here to make sure this stranger chooses himself a suit.' The Expert nodded wisely and shuffled through his papers.

'Come on, man, speak up! Say what you want, and we'll have it made up for you at once.'

'But I don't want a suit,' I said. 'In my country people don't wear disguises.'

The Expert looked at me over the top of his gold-rimmed glasses. 'All human beings wear suits,' he said coldly 'but I have heard that they are sometimes invisible.'

He cleared his throat. 'Surely you must be aware that you're acting a part sometimes?'

I was just about to argue with him when I suddenly 'saw' myself lolling in an alehouse, tankard in hand, wench on my knee, while I kept everyone laughing with endless funny stories. I always played that joker every time I went out with my mates, just to make them like me, but it was no more real than any of those funny disguises.

So I smiled at the Expert and the General, and I said, 'Perhaps I have in the past, but thanks to you lot I'm going to be Plain Sam Salt from now on. Why don't the rest of you get those ridiculous suits off and start being real too?'

'This man is dangerous,' said the Expert. 'He must be deported instantly!'

So I found a ship later that day and came back to tell King Paxalom about my adventures. But one thing's for sure: I owe a lot to those crazy people, I can tell you!

No one clapped. The knights sat in silence for a long time and then, one after another, they got up from the Octagonal Table and began to take off their armour.

13
The Girl in the Cage

It is for freedom that Christ has set us free.
Stand firm, then, and do not let yourselves be
burdened again by a yoke of slavery. (Galatians
5:1)

There was once a young man called Ferdinand, who was
left a fortune when his father died. He had a fine house,
estates, horses and beautiful possessions, but he was bored.

'My servants do everything better than I do,' he said. So
he set off to see the world on the finest stallion money
could buy.

As he rode through a dark forest one evening he came to
a castle hidden in the trees. It looked a gloomy, sinister
place, but as it was getting late, and he had no wish to be
lost in the forest, he decided to ask for shelter.

The lady of the castle herself opened the great oak door;
she was so monstrously tall and imposing that Ferdinand
began to feel like a naughty schoolboy who couldn't do his
sums. His fine clothes and good horse seemed to satisfy

her, so she welcomed him graciously. That night he slept well in spite of the owls, bats and black cats that shared his bedchamber.

Next morning he was just about to leave when his hostess asked if he would like to see her greatest treasure. Ferdinand was restless; he disliked the atmosphere of this castle and he had more than enough treasure of his own. But there was something about the woman that made him follow her as meekly as a lamb. When she opened the door of the largest room in the castle, Ferdinand was astonished to see that it was almost completely filled by a gigantic cage with bars of iron. Inside, it was beautifully furnished with a bed, comfortable chairs, books and even a golden harp. Ferdinand was just trying to think what to say when he saw the most beautiful girl he had ever seen in his life standing in the centre of the cage.

'That is my daughter,' said the woman proudly. 'Isn't she lovely?'

'Yes indeed!' agreed Ferdinand. 'But why do you keep her in a cage?'

'There are so many dangers in the world, and in the castle too,' replied the woman. 'She's safer in the cage.'

'But doesn't she miss walking in the gardens, sitting on the grass or lying under a tree? And what about the sky and the clouds – or even the sea?' He stopped and bit his lip; he had never realised that a girl's beauty could make him sound like a soppy poet!

'Oh no!' laughed her mother. 'You don't miss what you've never had, and she hasn't been out of that cage since the day she was born. You like feeling safe, don't you dear?' she said, smiling indulgently through the bars. The girl nodded and smiled too, but her dimples were Ferdinand's undoing.

Somehow he managed to extend his visit to a month, and spent every day talking to the girl through the bars, writing her poetry or listening for hours as she played her harp. At last he said to her mother, 'I would give everything I have to set your daughter free!'

'Everything?' said the woman with a cunning smile. Lowering her voice she whispered, 'You can have her in exchange for all that you possess.'

Five weeks later Ferdinand returned to the castle leading an ox cart weighed down with golden coins. He had sold mansion, land and possessions, but he was so wildly in love that nothing mattered to him except the girl in the cage. He was singing as he marched over the drawbridge.

The woman insisted on counting the coins and biting every one with her yellow teeth before she led him to her daughter's cage.

'Here you are,' she said, handing him an iron key, and hurried off to count her money over again.

'I've come to set you free!' exclaimed Ferdinand, bounding into the cage like a dancer making a stage entrance. 'Come, my darling, let me show you the sky, the moon, the mountains . . .' The speech he had rehearsed so often petered out as she cowered away into the far corner of the cage. 'I thought you loved me,' he faltered.

'Oh, I do!' she cried. 'But I'd rather you stayed here in the cage with me. I'd be too frightened to go out.'

'But I've given everything I had to win your freedom,' he said.

'But I'd much rather *not* be free,' she replied with a sniff. Ferdinand knew there was only one thing to do, so before her mother came back he swept his bride-to-be into his arms and carried her, protesting loudly, out of her prison.

As he hurried over the drawbridge, she caught her first sight of the forest. Terrified, she fell into a swoon. Hastily he wrapped her in blankets in the back of the ox cart and rode away as fast as the elderly animal could carry them.

Three days later she still had not moved, but by then they had reached the seaside and Ferdinand had found them an empty fisherman's cottage on the shore.

'The first things she'll see are the waves crashing up the beach and the clouds drifting overhead,' he thought happily. 'What a beautiful place for a wedding.'

But when she finally opened her eyes and found herself propped up among the sand dunes, she screamed in terror for an hour and then swooned again.

'I'll try the woods next time she wakes,' thought Ferdinand. 'We can be married on the moss beneath the great oak trees.' He thought that sounded most romantic, but the poor girl thought the birds would attack her, the trees would fall on her and the moss would give her a cold. So following the briefest of ceremonies they returned hurriedly to their hut. It was small, dark and extremely damp, but she was much happier once the door and windows were tightly shut.

For the next few months she stayed inside, scrubbing the floors, cooking meals for Ferdinand and darning his clothes, but she never went out herself. He caught fish and grew vegetables but his bride refused to eat anything at all. When he tramped for hours to the market and brought home delicacies to tempt her appetite, she refused every one.

'You'll die if you don't eat something soon!' he exploded one day when he saw how thin and ill she looked.

'Can't you see I'm afraid?' she shouted back at him. Afraid of that big sea out there and the forest, but most of all I'm afraid of food! I wish I was safely back in my cage. I didn't choose to come here.'

'You didn't *choose* to be put in that cage in the first place,' Ferdinand pointed out.

'That's just it!' she replied. 'I've never been allowed to make any choices for myself in life. What I eat or don't eat is the only little area of my life where I have any control at all!'

'All I wanted was for you to be free,' protested Ferdinand.

'Then give me freedom *not* to eat and *not* to go out!'

'But there's such a beautiful world out there for us to enjoy together,' sobbed poor Ferdinand. 'I gave everything I had to set you free from your prison, but all you've done is exchange it for another, which is far smaller and much less comfortable!'

'But can't you see that I need to be in a prison in order to feel safe?'

Baffled and badly hurt, Ferdinand walked for hours up and down the beach, biting his fingers in sheer desperation. 'How can I stand by and let her choose to starve herself to death?' he asked himself over and over again.

Then he had an idea. 'I'll go to the king,' he told the seagulls. 'I've heard he has wonderful powers.'

When Ferdinand arrived at the palace, King Paxalom was extremely busy. Piles of papers littered his desk; his Lord

Chamberlain was trying to push still more under his nose and the Knights of his Octagonal Table stood over him, making suggestions and giving advice. When a pageboy announced that someone wanted to see the king urgently, the knights shooed him away, but King Paxalom beckoned to the boy. 'What does this man want from me?' he asked.

'Sire, he has a very sick wife. He seems so desperate that I should not like to tell him to go away.'

'No more should I,' said Paxalom and, scattering papers in all directions, he stood up. 'Tell him I will see him at once.' Sir Marmaduke made a noise like the snort of a frustrated bull, but he managed to turn it into a polite cough, just in time.

'A king is no longer worthy of his crown when he ceases to give the needs of individuals paramount importance,' said Paxalom as he strode out of the room, ignoring the fluster of irritation he had caused.

He listened to Ferdinand's tragic story without interrupting.

'She will be dead soon, Your Majesty,' finished the young bridegroom. 'She is afraid of life itself. Please, is there anything you can do?'

'The prison bars of fear are far stronger than iron bars,' said Paxalom thoughtfully. 'It sounds to me as if your mother-in-law has trapped her daughter since early childhood. Bring her here to me at this time tomorrow.'

'But Your Majesty, she will not come. Perhaps I should drag her here by force?'

'No, she has the right to choose,' replied Paxalom. 'Dragging her here would be useless.'

'Then perhaps Your Majesty could give me some

medicine to take to her? Or even . . . perhaps . . . you might condescend to come yourself?'

'Going into her "cage" with her would never bring her healing,' replied Paxalom. 'Her healing can only begin when she chooses to walk out of it.'

'But sire, she doesn't know you, so how could she possibly trust you enough to walk away from where she feels safe?'

For a long time Paxalom stood looking down into Ferdinand's anxious face, then at last he said, 'Your wife is very fortunate to have such a persistent husband. I like you for that, Ferdinand. I shall ride with you to your home at once. As you say, your wife cannot trust me until she knows me better.'

The Knights of the Octagonal Table shook their heads sadly as they watched their king ride away with Ferdinand. 'No sense of priority,' they agreed. 'One silly girl is more important to him than all the weighty affairs of state!'

When they reached the hut by the sea, they were met at the door by the girl's mother. She gave Ferdinand a withering look as she announced grandly, 'I have come to take my daughter home; she will be safer with me, back in her cage. Kindly keep away. You will only upset her.'

She was so used to being obeyed without question that when she found herself face to face with King Paxalom her astonishment was almost comical. He was even taller than she was and far more intimidating.

She left hurriedly.

The girl was lying on her bed, almost unconscious from starvation, but she looked up at Paxalom with two huge frightened eyes.

'Yes,' he said softly, 'it is fear that traps you, little one. Fear has become your prison but also your safe hiding place. The best antidote to fear is love! I learned that from an old doctor I met many years ago. He used to put his hands on the heads of his patients so that he could pour love right through their whole bodies.'

'Did that make them well?' she whispered.

'Only if they were willing to open their hearts to that love,' replied Paxalom. 'And some were not. Are you willing, my dear?' She made no reply so he continued gently, 'If you allow love to fill your heart, it begins to push out those bars of fear until they break completely – and you will be free.'

'Yes, I want that,' she whispered. 'Can you do it to me now?'

'No,' he replied softly. 'First you have to choose to walk out of your safe cage and leave it behind.'

'But I'm too afraid to go out,' she sobbed.

'What are you afraid will happen if you leave this cottage? Do you fear people will hurt you?'

'Oh no, I know there isn't *really* anything to fear, but I know I'll be afraid anyway.'

'So the only thing you fear is the feeling of fear itself,' said Paxalom. 'But if I were to tell that fear to go, then you might be able to come and visit me tomorrow at noon?'

'I can't imagine what it would feel like not to be afraid,' she said simply, 'but yes, sire, I'm willing to try anything.'

Suddenly Paxalom's voice seemed to fill the tiny room as he stood, towering over her bed, 'In the name of love I set you free from the bondage of fear!' he boomed, and then, dropping to his knees beside her, he added more softly,

'Tomorrow we will positively flood your heart with love, but first you need two vital things.' Putting his hand lightly on her head he said, 'I impart to you my own courage and my own zest for life, so that, in future, you will want to choose life and freedom.'

For a long time Paxalom continued to kneel beside her with his hand on her head. She had fallen into a deep sleep long before he left. On the doorstep he turned and said to Ferdinand, 'I shall send one of the queen's litters to fetch her tomorrow morning; she's not strong enough to walk.'

'Oh sire,' whispered Ferdinand, 'what if she won't . . .?'

Paxalom put his hand gently on the young man's shoulder. 'That's her battle,' he said. 'We can't fight it for her, but if she wins, the prize is life and happiness for both of you!'

The following day, as the clock struck twelve, Paxalom was standing rather anxiously on the main drawbridge of his castle. 'The poor girl's fighting for her life,' he said as the minutes ticked slowly by.

'Your Majesty, surely you should come in now,' said Sir Marmaduke an hour later. 'It's cold out here, and obviously your visitors have decided not to come.'

'I shall wait just a little longer,' sighed Paxalom, but after another half an hour he went sadly back to his desk.

When he looked out of his window for the tenth time, two hours later, he saw a litter moving slowly down the road towards the castle. 'They're coming!' he shouted, and beaming all over his face he ran down the stairs at such a speed he was on the drawbridge before they reached it.

'You did it!' he said, beaming with delight. 'Well done!'

'I'm afraid it was rather a long battle,' admitted Ferdinand apologetically.

'But I won it in the end!' added his wife.

'Welcome to life and all its many joys!' said Paxalom, as he led the way into the palace.

They spent a delightful day being entertained as if they had been royalty, because Paxalom believed in practical, as well as spiritual, love! Before they finally left, he appointed Ferdinand Fisherman to the Royal Household and gave him a bag of gold with which to buy a boat and build his wife a better house.

In the years that followed Paxalom and Sophia often visited the cosy little house by the seashore. Ferdinand's wife cooked them delicious oatcakes and freshly caught herrings, and there was nothing the king liked better than making sand castles on the beach with her three happy children.

14

Dungeons and Mice

So do not fear, for I am with you; do not be
dismayed, for I am your God. I will strengthen
you and help you; I will uphold you with my
righteous right hand. (Isaiah 41:10)

Queen Sophia disliked Mondays. The king always spent
the day with his knights in the council chamber, and she
never saw him until the evening. She would take her
sewing into the ante-chamber, so she could at least hear his
voice through the door. She could never make out what
anyone was saying, but she found the drone of male voices
most soothing.

One Monday, however, their discussion sounded anything but relaxing. Fists banged on the Octagonal Table,
chairs scraped the stone floor and voices boomed with passion. When eventually the knights stamped angrily out in
search of refreshment, they looked positively dishevelled.
Sophia hastily ordered a large glass of wine and led her
exhausted husband up to their private sitting room.

'Dear, dear!' he sighed, as he settled himself by the fire. 'I wish those knights of mine were as sensible as they are bold. Can you guess what they were trying to make me do this morning? Invade the Land of Utter Desolation! Even an army as vast as ours would be lost for good in that dismal forest!'

'Do you always choose your knights for their fiery courage?' smiled Sophia.

'It depends on what you mean by courage,' replied Paxalom. 'Take Sir Cat, for instance.'

'Tell me about him,' said Sophia, not because she really wanted to know but telling a story always relaxed him more quickly than anything else.

'Well,' began Paxalom, stretching his feet towards the fire, 'most people would never describe Sir Cat as a brave man. But I would disagree. One of my barons had five huge sons and it was obvious from babyhood that they would all be fine soldiers – they fought from morning till night. Those five sons had a little brother, the youngest, who really ought to have been born a girl. He had golden curls and big blue eyes and he was frightened of everything from the day he was born. How those big boys teased him. He couldn't sleep without a light; he didn't like dogs; he panicked in crowds and was terrified of being shut in cupboards; but most of all he feared mice. The very thought of them petrified the poor child. One day his brothers put a dead one in his empty shoe and when he found it he fainted on the spot. They enjoyed the joke so much they told it to everyone who ever came to the house, and always finished by saying, "When our little brother grows up, he's going to be a cat."'

'Poor little thing!' snorted the queen.

'You're right,' laughed Paxalom, 'he *was* a little thing when I first met him. He would have been about ten but he was as small as a five-year-old and always apologising, even for things that weren't his fault! Anyway, the baron, their father, was a pushy kind of man and he wanted to establish at least one of his sons in my household, with the hope that he would eventually become a Knight of the Octagonal Table. It was soon after I became king and I needed a new page, so I told the man to bring all his sons to the palace so I could choose one of them for the post. The five older boys stood in a row in front of me, and a very fine bunch they looked – but it was difficult to get to know them while they were standing so stiffly to attention. So I sat them down with a jug of ale and tried to make them talk.

'"Do you have any sisters at home," I asked.

'"No," they told me, "but we do have a brother who looks just like a girl."

'"Where is he?" I asked, remembering that I had asked the baron to bring *all* his sons to see me.

'"He's outside in the stables, taking care of our horses."

'"Fetch him," I said, and in he came. Poor lad, he looked as if he thought I was going to cut off his head! One of the older boys began to tell me their favourite story, and as he finished with "and when our brother grows up he's going to be a cat!" they all laughed heartily, but I did not join them. I hated to see the shame on that poor little boy's face. So I turned to the baron and said, "I've made my choice. I'll have your youngest son as my page." I can't think why I did it. Perhaps it was simply to teach those arrogant youths a lesson – they certainly looked extremely cross.

'"Well, Master Cat," I said, "will you be my page boy?" The thought of coming to court so appalled him that he fainted once again and I began to regret my hasty decision.'

'Was he a good page?' asked Sophia.

'No, he was appalling! He was so afraid of doing something wrong that he used to hide so I couldn't ask him to do anything, but I think he grew quite fond of me in time.'

'Most people do,' smiled Sophia.

'Well, late one night, when I had been working long hours at my desk and most of the servants had long since gone to bed, I found I was ravenously hungry. This page had fallen fast asleep at his post, so I woke him and told him to go down to the larder and fetch me some bread and cheese. He turned green with fear and flung himself on his knees.

'"Sire, I beg you, don't send me to the larder!" He sounded as if I were sending him to his execution. "Ask another boy! Please, Majesty."

'"I can't," I replied, pulling him to his feet by his shirt collar. 'They're all in bed. I want *you* to go."

'"But sire, they tell me there are . . . are . . . mice in the larder!" He whispered the word as if the very sound of it were more than he could bear.

'"Probably there are," I agreed. "But if the very worst should happen and one runs up your leg, would it matter?"

'He swayed on his feet and I thought he would swoon again, but instead he managed to say, "Oh yes, Majesty, it *would* matter, for I would die of fright."

'"But suppose one ran up your leg and you didn't die?

Would that not be a wonderful discovery?" His teeth began to chatter and his eyes rolled horribly.

'"Master Cat," I said at last, "I think you are the bravest person I have ever met." That surprised him so much he stopped shivering and gaped at me. "No one else has ever dared to disobey me before. So what shall I do? Shall I have you whipped for insubordination?"

'Even that plan did not work; he actually looked rather pleased. "Oh yes, Your Majesty," he said, "have me whipped as hard as you like, but please don't send me to the larder." So I sent him to bed instead and went to fetch my own supper. I couldn't help liking him, but I knew I would have to cure him of his fears, somehow.

'One January, not long before I met you, my dear, I had to visit a distant cousin of mine. He lives in a large and very draughty castle on the coast and it is so cold that all my servants hate going there. So, to avoid their grumbles, I only took a few, and this page was one of them. I hoped the winter gales might toughen him.

'Unfortunately for Sir Cat the castle cellars were infested with mice and rats. Once the castle servants suspected my page's fear they teased him mercilessly. "There are so many of them down there," they told him, "they cover the ground like a seething mass, and crawl all over anyone who goes down there." The boy was so terrified he was quite unable to sleep or eat.

'One evening my cousin and I stayed up very late swapping hunting stories, and enjoying some excellent wine. We sent all the servants to bed and just kept this page up to wait on us. He was standing behind my chair, as every good page should, when the doors of the dining room burst open and two huge ruffians barged in, brandishing evil-looking knives. They grabbed me, and before I could reach my sword I was bound hand and foot. I looked to my cousin for help, but he stood there laughing at me.

' "Now I have you in my power," he said. "I have always wanted to be king in your place." They dragged me out of the room and down into the castle cellars. I didn't need a gag; no one would have heard my cries for help right down there below the castle, and my useless page had hidden himself under the table.'

'Did you see any mice?' shuddered the queen.

Paxalom looked pained. 'My dear, I was about to be murdered – mice were the last thing on my mind! They threw me down on the ground by the castle well and my cousin stood over me, gloating. "We're going to cut the throat of every one of your servants," he hissed, "and then, when I'm sure there is not one left to see, we'll come back and throw you down this well! Tomorrow I shall ride to the capital and have myself crowned king!"

'I knew my people would never have him as their king – he's far too lazy – but he wasn't to know that before he'd killed me. Off he went with his henchmen, leaving me lying there helpless.'

'On the floor with all those mice!' said the queen with another shudder. 'And in the dark too.'

'Well, it wasn't quite dark,' admitted Paxalom. 'High up above my head there was one square of light, coming from a small window. Suddenly, I saw a face looking down at me. It was the page.

' "Come here quickly!" I ordered. "Untie me before they get back. At least I can give my cousin a fight before he steals my crown. Can you find the door of this prison? I didn't hear them bolting it."

'"Sire," said he, and I could hear his teeth chattering, "I couldn't possibly come in there and untie you."

'"You would leave your king here to die just because you are afraid of a little mouse?" I shouted furiously. "Come down at once, and show your courage."

'"But I . . . h . . . h . . . haven't any courage, sire," he said.

'"Courage isn't about not being afraid," I roared. "Courage is being afraid but doing it anyway!" His face disappeared and I actually thought he was on his way to help me. But no, he was only being sick, and my last hope died.

'Much later the door of the cellar opened a tiny crack. My page had brought a flaming torch that he thrust inside, obviously hoping to frighten the mice away, but unfortunately the sudden light caused such a scurry of vermin that he screamed and dropped the torch.

'"Come back in here at once!" I yelled.

'"But Majesty, I saw them! They had terrible yellow teeth and awful red eyes!"

'"That's just imagination, lad," I said. "Come on – the thing you fear always gets bigger when you run away, but much smaller when you walk towards it." He picked up the torch, very gingerly, and began creeping across the stone floor towards me.

'Then the worst happened!'

The queen, who was cursed with a vivid imagination, jumped violently and covered her head with a cushion.

'Yes,' continued Paxalom without showing her any mercy, 'several mice ran right up his legs and inside his shirt.'

With a strangled cry the queen put her fingers in her ears. Raising his voice Paxalom continued, 'I was sure he would run away, but such was his remarkable devotion to his lord and master, he ran towards me instead – even with the mice racing round inside his shirt! He managed to cut the ropes that bound me just before my cousin came back into the room.'

'Did he kill you?' asked the queen, peeping suspiciously out from under the cushion.

'No,' said Paxalom, 'but he laughed so loudly everyone in the castle must have been woken up!'

Sophia glared at her husband indignantly. 'You and your horrid cousin planned the whole thing,' she said, 'just to tease your poor page.'

'Well, we did arrange that little charade,' admitted Paxalom, looking a little ashamed of himself, 'but it was not to tease, I promise you. It cured the boy; it really did. He discovered that even though the thing he dreaded most actually took place, he survived. When you have lived through your worst fear nothing else bothers you very much afterwards. He soon found that all the other things that frightened him had also lost their power. I praised his bravery so loudly and so often that he stopped thinking of himself as a cringing little mouse, waiting to be trodden on by everyone.

'When he walked towards me in the dungeon, when everything in him must have wanted to run away, he displayed as much courage as any I've seen in the Knights of my Octagonal Table. So once he was old enough I dubbed him Sir Cat the Brave and he has lived up to his title ever since.

'But,' finished Paxalom severely, 'I do feel a little hurt, my dear, that you seemed far more worried about a mere boy than you were about your husband who was facing a horrible fate!'

'But of course!' she replied. 'I would much rather be thrown to my death down a well than have even one small mouse in my shirt!'

15
The Ugly Princess

I will give you a new heart and put a new spirit
in you; I will remove from you your heart of
stone and give you a heart of flesh. (Ezekiel
36:26)

Not everyone loved Good King Paxalom; his only daughter
said she hated him. 'You're always so good it gets on my
nerves!' she said crossly. Her mother irritated her because
she was beautiful, and her brother and cousin because they
were boys.

'It's not fair!' complained Princess Margarita-Sophia. 'All
girls are allowed to do is sew and play the lute!'

As she could do neither she also complained she was
bored! She hated her maids-in-waiting because they were
slim and blonde, but most of all she loathed being a
princess. 'I wish I lived in a cottage!' she would moan.

'You don't know how lucky you are!' said the queen,
who knew from experience how uncomfortable cottages
could be.

'She was born in a bad temper,' sighed her mother, 'and she's been angry ever since.'

'If only she knew how much she was loved,' the king would say sadly.

'She doesn't *want* to be loved,' declared the exasperated queen.

By the time the princess was eighteen she was angrier than ever.

'She always was a plain child,' the courtiers would whisper, 'but now she's downright ugly!'

'I don't care!' she would say, glaring at herself in the mirror. She sent away her mother's hairdressers and cut her own hair until it looked as if moths had chewed it. She refused to wear the beautiful gowns the court dressmaker created for her, and she ate so many sweetmeats she grew fat and spotty. She began to be known as Princess Mags, because a beautiful name just didn't seem to fit her; only her father still called her Margarita-Sophia.

In spite of her appearance suitors still flocked to ask for her hand in marriage. She was the only daughter of the richest king in the world, so her dowry was most attractive, even if she was not! Mags said it amused her to see their eager expressions change when they first caught sight of her; but she would grind her teeth furiously when she overheard them laughing behind her back.

'She is quite the ugliest princess in the world,' sniggered the son of a sultan. But all the mercenary suitors proposed to her – despite her appearance.

'I hate the whole lot of them!' she declared. 'I won't marry at all.' So Mags began snubbing them all so ruthlessly she was soon famous for her rudeness as well as her looks.

Then one day she had such a dreadful row with her mother, she changed her mind and vowed to marry the next man who asked her. When he happened to be good looking she was considerably relieved.

'But I'm afraid I don't trust him,' King Paxalom told her. 'His father was a tyrant who treated his people with terrible cruelty, and now I've heard this young man is so short of money his army hasn't been paid for a year. An alliance with me is probably the last hope of saving his crown.'

'I don't care,' replied Mags. 'I want a palace of my own. I'm sick of being trapped here.'

She regretted her hasty decision almost as soon as she and her new husband rode away after the wedding; his charming smile slid from his face like melting grease.

'You're a spoilt brat!' he said harshly. 'I feel sick every time I look at you.'

When they arrived at his crumbling palace, she was given two small rooms in a turret and told to keep out of the way. 'My mistress and I like the whole palace to ourselves,' he said to her, and added cruelly, 'She's a very beautiful woman. She'll look lovely in all those wedding clothes your parents gave you, and they'll be no use to you up here. No one's going to see you.'

She was so angry she screamed all night, but no one heard her. The rooms were cold and bare, and she was given no ladies-in-waiting, only an old woman who was even worse tempered than she was.

'I'll write to my father!' she stormed at her husband when he came to visit her. 'He'll come with his army and crush you!'

Mags wrote often but she did not realise that all her

letters were read by her husband's chief spy, a clever wizard, who rewrote them so well that King Paxalom was delighted to hear how happily his daughter had settled into her luxurious palace. His loving replies, for which she waited each day, never reached her – the wizard saw to that.

'Why doesn't he come and rescue me?' she cried as the months dragged by and her hope began to die. 'I miss him so much. I'd give anything to be home with him again.'

All she had to do all day was eat, which she did almost continuously. From her window she could see over the great sprawling city that surrounded the palace. She noticed how hungry and poor the people seemed, victims of her husband's cruelty and neglect, but she would willingly have changed places with any of them.

The only time she was allowed to leave her turret was when a visiting ruler paid them a state visit. Her husband did not want rumours to reach King Paxalom that his daughter was a prisoner, so during state banquets she always sat at his right hand; and it was on one such occasion that Mags fell in love for the first time in her life. It was not the visiting crown prince who attracted her but her husband's younger brother. He would have been very tall if it had not been for the hump on his back, and he might have been handsome without the thick glasses through which he peered out at the world. Because he spent his life reading books in the palace library he was known as Randolph the Scholar, but few people ever spoke to him because of his dreadful stutter.

Mags had never spoken to him either, but in the middle of the crown prince's banquet she upset her wine all over him. Her husband struck her viciously, much to the astonishment of their royal guest, but Randolph's look of utter compassion provided her with endless material for her daydreams. In them she always managed to poison her husband so Randolph would be crowned in his place and then, of course, he always married her. It kept her happy until one bad day it dawned on her that Randolph may only have smiled at her absentmindedly, as scholars do. Suppose he did not love her at all? If he ever became king he would probably find someone beautiful to marry. The very idea sent her into a pit of misery until she made a big decision: she would become beautiful herself and captivate his heart.

'How could such a thing be done?' she wondered, and then she remembered her father's magic elixir.

'Dear Father,' she wrote, 'I know you can do almost anything, but could you possibly make me beautiful?'

She doubted if he would reply; after all, he had not written once since her wedding. But she sealed it with a kiss and hoped for the best. When the wizard vetted the letter, he shrugged and let it go. To him, the queen looked so revolting she constituted a national disgrace, so he reckoned any help had to be better than nothing.

Paxalom sat for a long time with his daughter's letter in his hand. Could her heart be softening at last? he wondered, and he began to feel a tinge of hope.

'My dear,' he wrote back, 'to me you have always been beautiful! My elixir will certainly help you, but only very slowly, because what you describe as your "ugliness" is caused by the bitterness in your heart – and hearts take a long time to heal. I have decanted some into this small bottle for you, but *do not take it yourself* – it would do you no good. But each time you administer a drop to someone else, who must be in desperate need, it will change your own heart as well.'

The wizard never had the chance to intercept Paxalom's reply. Since the affair of the Morbids, he had trained a golden eagle to carry urgent messages for him. So the elixir was delivered in a silken bag, and dropped safely through the turret window.

Mags was *not* pleased. 'The first letter he's bothered to write to me and all he can do is criticise and preach a sermon! That's typical of the sanctimonious old so and so,' and she flung the bottle down contemptuously onto her bed. Then she picked it up, burst into tears and hid the bottle in the pocket of her shabby old dress. She missed him so badly!

That day the army, who still had not been paid in spite of Mags' dowry, staged a coup. Their general, a burly knight called Sir Oswald, speared the king through his mean black heart when he came to inspect the barracks. Then, seizing his crown, he declared himself supreme ruler and marched off towards the palace, vowing to kill everyone connected with the royal family.

Mags heard the news with mixed feelings. She was delighted her husband was dead but terrified of sharing his fate, so she escaped from the palace through the sewers. When she emerged, people assumed she was a beggar. She was filthy and smelt appalling, she had lost her shoes in the drain and her hair hung from her head like dead rats' tails. No one expects queens to look like that, so she merged perfectly into the ragged crowds that filled the city streets. 'I'll stay here until my father comes,' she thought. 'Once he thinks I've been murdered he'll soon bring his armies to avenge me.'

Then it occurred to her that Randolph, the heir to the throne, would have been Sir Oswald's first target on reaching the palace. She wondered why she had bothered to escape since there seemed to be no point in living without him. The realisation that she would never again see his kind eyes peering at her through dusty spectacles caused her more anguish than she had ever known.

She was the only person who was sad in the city that day, for everyone else was cheering, 'We're free!' But their joy was soon crushed. It was the wicked wizard who had incited Sir Oswald, and freedom was not something he planned for anyone but himself.

Mags had never walked through the streets of a city before, particularly not the dark alleyways where the homeless camped out at night. The further she walked over the next few days, the angrier she became.

'How could any king allow his people to live like this?' she raged. The streets stunk with human excrement, thrown from the houses with other rubbish that rotted where it lay. She saw rats, mangey dogs and even pigs rooting in the filth beside hungry-looking children. She was constantly revolted by the sight of skin diseases, terrible injuries and festering wounds; and she often saw emaciated bodies lying, unburied, where they had died of starvation.

'How could that wicked man have sat in his palace so close to all this suffering?' she thought. 'If I ever escape I won't spend the rest of *my* life lazing about doing nothing.

I shall put a stop to this kind of thing!' Round and round the city streets she marched, muttering furiously; the anger that had always filled her heart was now giving her the energy to survive. The outrage she felt on behalf of these people also made her forget her own hunger, cold and sore feet. 'My father will arrive any day now,' she told herself.

She did not realise that the wizard had written to Paxalom, in her handwriting, saying that she and Sir Oswald had murdered her husband together and now intended to marry and rule jointly. He wept over that letter many times, but it was the last curt sentence that caused him the greatest pain: 'I don't want any further contact with you, so don't bother to come to the wedding.'

It was winter, and icy winds and sleet finally reminded Mags of her hunger. She felt begging was out of the question for a queen, so she was forced to scour the city rubbish dump instead. It was dusk when she heard angry shouts and the frightened cries of children coming from one of the many sordid shacks that surrounded the tip.

'I'm not having that!' she thought indignantly, as a large man appeared in a doorway, dragging a terrified woman by the hair.

'Get out!' he bellowed, as he kicked several small children into the gutter after the woman – and added a wailing baby to the heap. 'If you can't pay the rent, you don't stay!'

'Please sir, my husband will pay when he comes back. Don't turn us into the streets. The little ones will die.'

'When he comes back!' he snorted scornfully. 'He's been gone three weeks. He won't come back now!'

Blind rage filled Mags, and pulling herself up to her full height, which was considerable, she confronted the bully with her hands on her hips. 'How dare you!' she said in the terrible voice her father's servants had learned to dread. The blood of many warrior kings ran in her veins, but none of them had ever looked more formidable than Mags at that moment. 'Go away and leave this poor mother in peace, or you'll have me to reckon with.'

'Sorry, lady,' he muttered, backing away. He did not stop to wonder who this awesome woman could be, and Mags did not wait to see if her orders were obeyed. She picked up the baby and helped the other children back into the hut.

The woman seemed unable to do anything but gaze at Mags in awe, so Mags settled the baby on a heap of rags in the corner and set about relighting the meagre fire. 'Don't just stand there, woman!' Mags ordered crossly. 'Get these children some supper.'

'I've nothing for them, lady,' was the dull reply.

Picking up two of the children, Mags strode purposefully back into the streets. The market stalls were being packed up for the night, but she charged up to one of the traders like a warhorse going into battle.

'It is vital that you give me some turnips to feed these starving children,' she said imperiously. The man was so surprised, he handed them over without a word, and even added an onion.

'Now I need a cooking pot and some water,' she said, returning to the shack, quite forgetting she had never cooked anything in her life.

The pot was soon filled from the filthy drain outside.

'Children need something warm in their tummies at bedtime,' she told the woman severely. The fact that she had never been near a child in her life seemed to have escaped her.

When everyone was fed, it did not seem to occur to the woman to ask Mags to leave, so they both lay down together on the floor by the embers, holding the children in their arms to keep them warm. All night the baby coughed and struggled for breath. By morning he finally lay silent and still in his mother's arms.

Mags was about to say, 'At least that's one less mouth to feed,' but there was something about the anguish in the woman's eyes that touched her hard heart and caused a strange new sensation. She had never felt anything like it before, but she found herself remembering that look of compassion Randolph had given her once. Tears stung her eyes and she dug in the folds of her dirty skirt for the handkerchief princesses and queens always keep in their pockets. Instead her fingers closed round a small glass bottle. The elixir! One drop could bring back the dead; she had seen it happen before.

'Would you like me to make your baby well?' she asked in the gentlest voice she had ever used.

'Oh yes,' gasped the woman. 'He's the only boy, you see and so like my poor husband.'

Unstopping the bottle, Mags moistened her finger with the elixir and pushed it into the baby's mouth. Almost at once he opened his eyes and his white cheeks soon became rosy.

'He's never been this healthy in his life!' exclaimed his mother when he began to yell lustily for his food. 'You're a miracle worker!'

'What's the point of miracles if we have no food for

hese children?' snapped Mags crossly. She was ravenous
erself, but she could see the children would not last many
nore days on turnip water.

'Come on!' she told them all sternly. 'Help me give this
place a good spring clean, and then we might have a hope
of keeping you well.'

Once they had swept and scrubbed the floor, and beaten
he mats outside in the street, she sent the older ones to
cour the rubbish dump for anything that might burn,
vhile she set off to bully the market traders into parting
vith their scraps.

She arrived back at the hovel, well pleased with her suc-
ess, to find a crowd of ragged women clustered round the
loor, each one holding a sickly baby or a dying child.

'Good Mother,' they implored, bowing respectfully,
please cure our children too.' She was tired and hungry for
he titbits in her bundle, but how could she eat while they
ooked on, starving, and their children whimpered with
pain? So she treated them all with her father's elixir, and
ven shared her supper.

Over the next few weeks it seemed to make no differ-
nce how many times she used the elixir – the bottle
efilled itself automatically. She did not realise that it was
nade up from the tears she shed for the people around her,
ind the blood from her hands and feet when they were
ubbed raw and cut by her efforts to help them.

'If you weren't too lazy to carry your rubbish to the
lump, I'm sure there'd be less sickness,' she told the
crowds who came to her for help each day. Such was her
authority that soon no one in the city dared to throw
inything into the street, and the cobbles were swept

conscientiously each morning.

When a terrible fever epidemic broke out on the far side of the city they sent a deputation to the door of the hovel.

'Please,' they asked humbly, 'come to heal our well. We think the water is poisoned.'

'I'm not at all surprised!' snapped Mags. 'It's downright disgusting the way you city people throw dead cats and goodness knows what else into your water supply. I'll only come if you promise to train your people better.' They agreed and one spoonful of the elixir purified the water and halted the epidemic completely.

It was a few months later when one of the richest men of the city came to ask for her help. Wealthy families stayed in their grand houses beyond the city walls and usually never ventured into the squalid city streets; but this man was desperate. In his arms he carried his only son, who was at the point of death.

'I'll cure him,' said Mags, 'but it will cost you 400 loaves of bread a day. Have them distributed to the poor each morning in the market-place. And woe betide you if you ever fail!' Stunned by her outrageous demands the man had no choice but to agree.

Soon the rich were all flocking to her door. Most paid for their miracles by providing food for the poor, but others were told to give them firewood, warm clothes or bedding. The richer they were the more they were forced to give; some even agreed to build neat little houses to replace the revolting hovels and huts.

'Come and live out in the suburbs with us,' her rich patients urged Mags. 'You could have your own home and servants.' They would have given her anything, but Mags refused all their lavish presents with disdain, saying, 'I would never use my elixir to benefit myself!'

Many would have liked to steal the elixir but nobody dared; they were far too afraid of her supernatural powers!

She often wondered how long it would be before someone recognised her and told Sir Oswald where she lived. What she did not realise was that she was changing so rapidly no one could ever have recognised her. After two years with little food and much hard work, her fat was gone and so were her spots. Even her hair had grown long and curly. For the first time in her life she knew she was respected, so now she walked with dignity and grace.

Yet it was her face where the most striking difference had taken place. King Paxalom always used to say, 'The state of the heart can be read in the face.' Every time she helped someone else, willingly and without complaint, a drop of bitterness drained from her heart. It was instantly replaced by a similar amount of love, which gave a sweetness to her mouth and wiped the frown from her forehead. She was still often angry, but only on behalf of others, and this served to make her eyes sparkle and her cheeks glow. She had, in fact, become very beautiful.

One morning, as she hurried to market, an old woman pulled at her ragged cloak. 'Please come and help my son. He's dying,' she whispered urgently.

Mags did not hear her at first; she was smiling to herself as she remembered her visit to the mayor's house the previous day. He was so worried about his wife's health that Mags had been even more audacious than usual when stating her terms: 'A school, complete with teachers and books, for every quarter of the city.'

'What! Teach the poor to read and write? But why?' he had spluttered.

'If Prince Randolph had lived to become your king, that is what he would have wanted,' she had replied. And, as usual, she had her way.

'He's a good boy, mistress,' whimpered the crone. 'He can't help being a hunchback.' Mags stopped. Randolph had been a hunchback!

'I'll come at once,' she said softly, 'for his sake.'

'He was hurt by the soldiers the day the king was killed,' explained the old woman as she led the way down some steep cellar steps. 'The wounds turned bad and just wouldn't heal and now he seems to have lost the will to live.'

'I'm not surprised!' said Mags severely as she looked round the room; it was dark and damp and stunk of disease. 'You would be ashamed to keep a dog down here!'

'Where else is there?' muttered the woman, and lit a candle beside a filthy straw mattress. A man lay there, on his side, with his knees curled up to his chin. He peered up at Mags through thick dusty glasses.

'Randolph!' she whispered.

'Margarita-Sophia!' he said, and tried to say more but his stutter defeated him.

'I thought you were dead,' she said, flinging herself down on the stone floor beside him. He reached out and took her hand, still unable to speak.

'You're the queen?' said the old woman, amazed. Mags ignored her – she was weeping as she looked at the terrible open wounds all over Randolph's body.

'You must have been in so much pain,' she said tenderly.

'Those soldiers left him for dead in the library,' said the old woman. 'That's where I found him. He was my nursling as a child, and I still did his washing. It was quite easy for me to smuggle him out of the palace in my laundry basket, but he's suffered so terribly I've often wondered if it would have been kinder to leave him.'

'You did right, Good Mother,' said Mags, 'and better still to fetch me today. His pain is over at last,' she added as she opened her precious bottle and put one drop of the contents on Randolph's tongue. The effect was dramatic. In a moment he was standing straight and tall, his wounds healed and even the hump and stutter gone. Once he had removed his glasses, he could see perfectly and gazed down at Mags for so long she grew nervous.

'Am I . . . do you think I'm . . . just a little bit . . . more beautiful?' she asked at last.

'How can I tell?' he laughed. 'I've never been able to see you before. I assumed you were beautiful, but your appearance was unimportant – it was your indomitable courage that I loved. Most people would have been broken completely by what my brother did to you. I think I have loved you from the first day we met. But,' he finished, as he took her into his arms, 'now I can see you at last, I find that you are very beautiful indeed!'

'There's no time for this kind of thing,' said the old woman disapprovingly. 'Now you're well again, you're going to have to do something about Sir Oswald. He and that wizard of his are making all our lives a misery.'

'What am I supposed to do?' asked Randolph.

'You're the rightful king of this country, so it's your job to set us free,' she said firmly.

'But I don't want to be a king,' protested Randolph. 'Now I've found you again, Margarita-Sophia, all I want is to marry you, find a cottage in the mountains, full of books, and live happily ever after.'

'Oh yes?' said Mags tartly. 'And what am I supposed to do all day while you read your books?'

Randolph gave her a crooked smile. 'All right, a cottage in the mountains with no books – just you and me?'

But Mags was still looking thoughtful. 'Do you want me to be a king?' he suggested tentatively, but she shook her head.

'Good,' smiled Randolph, 'so let's live happily ever after, just the two of us.'

'Well, of course I'd like to marry you,' said Mags still rather crossly, 'but I've been given this special gift by my father. How could I live happily ever after while I knew there were people in pain and misery that I could ease by sharing that gift?'

Randolph burst out laughing. 'What a queen you would make!' he said. 'I'd better hurry up and fight Sir Oswald for my crown so you and I can reform the nation together!'

King Paxalom and Queen Sophia were sitting in their private garden; she was sewing, but the king sat silently gazing at nothing at all. The beauty of the flowers and birdsong was lost on him these days.

'My dear,' sighed Sophia reaching out to touch his hand, 'I hate to see you suffering like this. I know you miss Mags, but isn't it time you accepted the fact that she doesn't want us any more?'

Paxalom fumbled in his pocket for his daughter's last letter and read it for the thousandth time. 'I so hoped my elixir would work,' he said sadly. 'Perhaps it didn't reach her in time. I know she was sometimes a little difficult, but I love her so much. I cannot believe she could possibly murder her own husband.' Sophia shook her head sadly. She didn't like to say she could believe it quite easily.

Just then, the Lord Chamberlain himself came through the rose arch, bowing profusely. He knew their Majesties did not like to be disturbed in their private corner of the grounds so he apologised at length before he managed to say, 'A young man claiming to be King Randolph of Glubstein wishes to speak to you urgently.'

'King who . . . of *where*?' said Paxalom with a puzzled frown.

'He certainly doesn't look like a king to me,' said the Lord Chamberlain with a disdainful sniff, 'but there is a young woman with him who claims . . . claims to be . . . the Princess Margarita-Sophia herself. She isn't really like Her Royal Highness but . . . Perhaps you ought to see her before I have them both taken down to the dungeons?'

'Princess Margarita-Sophia?' said Paxalom springing to his feet with more enthusiasm than he had felt for more than a year. 'Bring these people here at once!'

Sophia and Paxalom were both on their feet, gazing anxiously across the wide lawn as their visitors approached. The young woman was plainly dressed and her hair fell loose about her shoulders like a peasant's, but even from a distance she was beautiful, and she walked like a queen.

'It certainly isn't Mags,' sighed Sophia, but Paxalom was already running over the grass, his long legs hardly seeming to touch the ground.

'You look wonderful!' he exclaimed as his arms enfolded his daughter. 'I *knew* my elixir would work.'

The joy of feeling closer to him than she had ever been in her life was so great that Mags sobbed like a tiny child. Picking her up, Paxalom carried her back to his seat. As a rebellious child she had never wanted to sit on his knee, but now it seemed the safest place in the whole world.

'And I presume you are Oswald,' said Sophia turning coldly to the young man.

'*Oswald*!' snorted Mags, her face still buried in Paxalom's shoulder. 'Whatever makes you think he's Sir Oswald?'

It was dark long before they had told their lengthy story. Servants had lit the lamps that hung from the trees over their heads and brought shawls for Sophia and her daughter.

'I think it must have been that wizard who intercepted and rewrote all your letters,' said Randolph. 'He and Oswald have caused my people so much pain.'

'They caused me a lot too,' said Paxalom grimly. 'It is quite time they were ousted from their stolen nest. I and my entire army are at your disposal, King Randolph. I think we should leave at first light.'

'Father,' said Mags shyly. 'There is something that must happen first – a wedding!'

'A royal wedding takes months to plan!' exclaimed Sophia, who had discovered that evening that this new daughter was far easier to love than the old one had ever been.

'No time,' said Paxalom firmly. 'We must take them by surprise before they hear we are on our way.'

The wedding that took place the following morning was

not the grandest royal wedding in history, but it was probably one of the happiest. The same afternoon the two kings set off at the head of a massive army. The bride insisted on joining them.

'I'm not going to be the sort of wife who always stays at home,' she told Randolph firmly.

'I wouldn't have married a wife who did,' he replied happily.

Their plan was to surround and besiege the city, but as soon as the people of Glubstein realised Randolph was alive, and that he and King Paxalom had come to their rescue, they rapidly disposed of the two tyrants and opened the city gates to welcome their new king.

As the royal cavalcade swept through the city walls, the mayor and leading citizens were waiting in prestigious rows to welcome their saviours. However, they were totally unable to make the lengthy speeches they had so carefully prepared, because they simply could not take their eyes off King Randolph's beautiful young queen. They all recognised the woman who had blackmailed every one of them so successfully!

'Thank goodness I finished building those schools in time,' sighed the mayor, wiping sweat from his brow.

How the people cheered Queen Margarita-Sophia as she rode through the streets beside her new husband.

'We always knew our Miracle Lady was a queen in disguise,' they told each other. 'Just look what she's done for our city!'

The royal couple really did live happily ever after. He created libraries and schools all over the country, while she gently bullied the rich into providing for the poor, and soon no one in the land lacked job, food or home. It would have surprised the scornful sultan's son who had nicknamed Mags 'the ugliest princess in the world' had he known she eventually went down in history as the most beautiful queen who ever lived.

16

The Menacing Mountains

I consider that our present sufferings are not worth comparing with the glory that will be revealed in us. (Romans 8:18)

'That's it! Yes . . . yes! Watch your feet!' King Paxalom was leaning so far out of the window that the knights assembled in the council chamber behind him were convinced he would topple out at any moment.

'I take it Prince Michael is practising his swordsmanship in the courtyard below,' said Sir Marmaduke, who had arrived a little late. The other knights sighed in resignation. It was most unlikely that any business would be done that morning. They all knew King Paxalom's only son was the apple of his eye, and they had to admit that the king had every right to be proud of him. Now he was twenty-five and had completed his education, he was already taking over many of his father's duties – and doing them all extremely well. However, it was in sport of any kind that the prince excelled.

'And if all that weren't enough,' thought Sir Marmaduke with a wry smile, 'he's good looking as well!' But he had to admit that no one could help loving Michael.

'I'm sorry, gentlemen,' said Paxalom apologetically, when he finally took his place at the Octagonal Table, 'but he's trying to perfect this new side-step technique all the Frenchmen are using these days.'

'It was actually about His Royal Highness that we wanted to see Your Majesty,' began Sir Marmaduke ponderously. 'We feel that perhaps . . . it might be time . . . that . . .'

'He settled down?' finished Paxalom. 'I suppose he really ought to be married at his age, but I'm not sure where he would fit a wife into his sporting calendar.' They all laughed politely and Paxalom promised to talk to Michael later that day.

He eventually found the prince by the lake, where he had been swimming with some of his gentlemen-in-waiting. Paxalom waved them away and abruptly came to the point. 'Time you were married,' he said. 'Succession and all that.'

The prince, who was rubbing his wet hair vigorously, dropped the towel and gazed at his father in horror. 'Married!' he exclaimed. 'But Father, I haven't met anyone I like yet.'

'Nonsense,' replied the king. 'It's your duty to take this matter seriously. All you need to do is meet some suitable princesses. I'll organise a series of grand balls and we'll send invitations to all the royal families who have daughters of the right age.'

The balls took place once a month throughout the summer, and the princesses came in their dozens. Every royal house was determined that their daughter would be the one to catch the prince's eye and bring them wealth and prestige through an alliance with his father. So each princess was more elaborately decked out than the last. Some made their entrance in carriages made of gold, while others were carried in flower-decked litters. One even arrived by air, two storks carrying her in a swing suspended from their beaks, but the unfortunate birds dropped her too soon and she landed in the lake!

The ball gowns were vast constructions of wire, frills and flounces; and each royal guest tried to have the widest skirt or the longest train. Some of the hairstyles and head-dresses were so enormous the princesses could hardly hold up their heads. Inside all this finery the girls themselves were so well hidden by jewels and cosmetics that it was difficult to believe they were human beings at all.

'I can't fall in love with a wax model, however beautiful she is,' Michael told his father miserably at the end of the last ball of the season. 'And anyway, they only want to marry me for the sake of a crown – they don't love *me*!'

'Love!' exclaimed Paxalom. 'Royalty doesn't marry for love!'

'You did, Father,' said the prince.

Paxalom looked startled and then he smiled. 'Very well! No more princesses,' he promised.

So all the barons and rich merchants in the empire were invited to bring their daughters to court. The young ladies fluttered their eyelashes, giggled and dropped their hankies whenever Michael walked by, but he found them all so boring the idea of spending his life with one of them depressed him horribly.

'They're all very nice,' he told his father apologetically, 'but I did so want my wife to love me for myself alone and not just for the things I can give her.'

'Love like that is hard to find when a young man is as rich as you are,' replied his father sadly.

The winter went by, and more girls came and went, but the prince was looking pale and even his sporting activities no longer interested him.

'Something seems to be troubling His Highness,' said the royal physician.

'And I think I know what it is,' replied Paxalom gloomily.

'Father,' said Michael one morning in early spring, 'I've been wondering if I could take a holiday, forget I'm a prince for a while, and travel about like any ordinary young man.'

King Paxalom shot him a keen look from under his shaggy eyebrows. 'You're hoping to find a girl who'll love you, just as you are, and not because you're a prince? Very well then, but remember: one day you will rule this empire, so you owe it to your people to marry the right girl – someone worthy to be their queen and mother of future monarchs. I will only let you go on one condition: if you find a girl who loves you, and if you manage to bring her back here to me *before* she has the slightest idea who you really are, then, and only then, will I give my consent for your wedding.'

It seemed a strange condition to Michael, but he trusted his father's wisdom, and the prospect of an adventure was making him feel better already.

Not long afterwards a plainly dressed young man, who might have been the son of a respectable merchant, left the palace – well before dawn. He rode the oldest horse in the royal stables and carried a generous bag of gold in his vest pocket.

'I'm taking a terrible risk,' muttered Paxalom as he watched the departure from the ramparts above, 'but it's high time that boy grew up.'

The prince was determined to travel as far as possible from his father's palace, to make sure no one would recognise him, so he set out for the furthest corner of the empire. The journey took weeks, for his path lay across wide dusty plains, dark treacherous forests and the craggy peaks of the Menacing Mountains. But it was springtime, the weather was good and he enjoyed himself enormously. The elderly horse did not! When the city that was their destination came into view the poor old creature died of exhaustion, and toppled into a convenient ditch. The prince was sad, but walked on towards the city to buy a newer model.

He was tucking into a good meal in a tavern, when a group of young men told him they had a horse for sale in the yard at the back. He was green enough to follow them, and before he could reach for his dagger, they had dragged him into a dark alley, beaten him badly and stolen everything he possessed. When they finally left him in the gutter he was unconscious and bleeding heavily.

When he opened his eyes, a girl was kneeling beside him. Her long golden hair brushed against his battered face and her large blue eyes surveyed him anxiously.

'You poor thing,' she said in the most beautiful voice he

had ever heard. Lying there, looking at her, Michael decided this girl, in her simple clothes, made all the over-dressed princesses and noblewomen look plain in comparison. 'Let me help you up,' she said. 'I only live over there.'

Her father, a cobbler, hurried out of his shop, and together they soon had the battered prince lying by a warm fire wondering if he had died and arrived in heaven! When he recovered, Michael offered to repay their kindness by staying for a while and helping with odd jobs. He swept the shop, ran errands and generally made himself useful in exchange for cabbage soup and hard black bread. In the end he stayed six months, but it had not taken six seconds for Michael and Serena to fall in love.

'I live with my father, far across the Menacing Mountains,' was all he would say about himself, but when he finally asked the cobbler for his daughter's hand in marriage, the old man beamed with pleasure.

'She couldn't find anyone I like more,' he said.

'There's just one problem,' said Michael awkwardly. 'I can't marry her here in the city. My father insists on meeting her first.'

The cobbler was dumbfounded. 'You want to drag my poor daughter across those terrible mountains,' he protested, 'and not even marry her first?'

'Trust me,' urged the prince. 'I promise I'll look after her.'

'There are wolves in those forests,' muttered the cobbler, but deep down he knew he could trust this young man, even with someone as precious as his daughter. So he grudgingly gave his consent, and the preparations began.

'Suppose when we get there,' said Serena anxiously, 'your father doesn't approve of me?'

'He will,' smiled Michael.

'Perhaps it might help if I took him a present?' she ventured uncertainly.

'What could you take?' asked the prince, thinking of the array of treasures that filled his father's palace.

'I could embroider a little purse for him – to hold all his money,' she said shyly, not realising how gigantic it would have to be to contain all the coins King Paxalom possessed! 'Look,' she said, reaching deep into the chest where she kept her clothes, 'my mother gave me this little piece of silk before she died. I've been saving it for something really special. I'll cut it into the shape of a heart because I know I'm going to love your father very much.'

The cobbler made his daughter a little pair of soft leather shoes, the finest he had ever sewn, and spent his meagre savings on a small brown donkey. 'Can't have my daughter walking all that way,' he said, as he tried not to let her see the tears in his eyes.

It was late autumn when they started their journey, but the sun was still warm. They were so happy – at first. Serena sat on her donkey, stitching away at the little purse, while Michael strode along beside her, whistling.

'You do love me, don't you?' he would often ask.

'Of course I do!' she would reply ecstatically. But love was easy at the beginning. It grew a little more difficult when they reached the centre of the plain, the hot sun scorched their bare heads, and dust blew up into their eyes and choked them.

'Just look at my sewing,' she cried in dismay. 'It's all sticky with sweat and caked with dust! Whatever will your father think of it?' But she still stitched on – until the rain began. Day after day it lashed down: dreary, wet and demoralising.

'Perhaps we should have waited until spring,' said Serena, whose needle was rusty. Even the donkey's ears drooped.

'But you do still love me, don't you?' asked the prince.

'Yes, of course. You know I'd go anywhere with you,' she replied – but she hadn't yet seen the Menacing Mountains.

The never-ending plains had seemed bad enough, but the forest was even worse. The trees made it so dark that Serena could only see to sew when they made their campfire each night. However, her hands shook with terror when the wolves howled, so she kept pricking her fingers and staining her work with blood.

The forests grew so deep and dark it was hard to see the path.

'I wish we hadn't come,' said Serena nervously. 'Suppose we get lost?'

'I know the way,' said the prince confidently. 'You do trust me, don't you?'

'Yes,' she replied, 'I think so.' But she did not sound so sure.

Then they reached the mountains.

'We're not going all the way up there, are we?' said the poor girl, looking up in dismay at the towering peaks.

'I'll be beside you all the way,' the prince assured her.

'Isn't there a way *round* them?' Serena pleaded.

'This is the only way to my father's house,' urged Michael.

'I don't think I can,' she said with a sniff. Tears were

falling all over her sewing, adding to its already messy appearance. 'Please take me home! I wish we'd stayed with Father.'

'But if you only knew how wonderful it will be when we get to *my* father's home!' said Michael. 'In my father's house are many rooms. Don't let your heart be so troubled. Believe in me – just a little bit longer.'

'I'll try,' she said with a muffled sob, but the donkey was more stubborn. He flatly refused to take one more step along the path that wound up the steep mountainside, so they left him with a woodcutter.

'I'll be glad of his company,' said the man, 'but surely you're not going over the Menacing Mountains at this time of year? Snow's on the way – wait till spring.'

'I'm afraid we can't,' replied the prince. 'I've been away too long already.'

While Serena was saying a tragic farewell to the donkey, the ungrateful animal nuzzled into her pocket and found her sewing. He had chewed several holes in it before she managed to wrench it out of his mouth.

The hard rocky path had soon worn Serena's shoes away, leaving her feet cut and bleeding. They had been climbing for many hours when it began to snow heavily and the path disappeared completely. Serena's cloak blew away in the gale and soon her fingers were frostbitten. The wolves sounded as if they were closing in for the kill.

'Are you sure we're still on the path?' she asked in desperation.

'I'll just go ahead and make sure,' Michael replied. 'You take a rest on this rock.'

'Don't leave me here alone!' Serena protested. 'How can I be sure you'll ever come back?'

'Because I love you,' he said. She was crying too much to reply.

He was gone a long time. The wind howled round her and the wolves sounded closer than ever.

'Just when I need him most, he's disappeared!' she cried. 'How could he treat me like this?'

In a blind panic she got up and began staggering in and out of the snowdrifts, but suddenly the ground in front of her was gone, and she found herself standing on the edge of a dark chasm.

'I'm here!' shouted the encouraging voice of the prince from the far side. 'I've found the path, but you're going to have to jump this gap, I'm afraid. Just leap into my arms: I promise I'll catch you!'

'This is too much!' she shouted indignantly as she peered down into the abyss below. 'How do I know you won't let me fall?'

'Because I promised I wouldn't! How could I possibly let you fall when I love you so much?'

'Love!' she yelled back furiously. 'If you call this love you've got a strange way of showing it!'

'Everything will be all right when I get you to my father's house. Just trust me a little bit longer!'

'Trust! Trust! Trust! Why do you keep going on about *trust?*'

'Your faith in me is more important than anything else in the world,' he replied, but so softly she did not hear.

'I just don't understand you!' screamed Serena indignantly, and Michael glared back across the ravine, equally angry.

'You don't *have* to understand me! All you need to do right now is trust me – and jump!'

So she did – simply because she realised she had no alternative.

It was merely dogged determination that took her up the last steep stretches of the mountain path. She felt no love at all. Even her sewing froze to a solid ball of ice in her pocket.

A few days later a sentry on duty at the palace gates saw a ragged vagrant hobbling towards him through the gloom of the snowy afternoon. He was carrying what looked like a bundle of rags.

'Be off with you!' he bellowed.

'Go at once to the king and tell him his son has returned,' said a voice the soldier recognised at once.

Two minutes later, Michael, with his unconscious burden still held tenderly in his arms, was ushered straight into the council chamber where the king and his knights were assembled round the Octagonal Table.

'Father, I've found a girl who loves me for myself alone,' he said, as he placed Serena gently on a gilded couch. 'She was willing to give all she had in this world, just for me.'

Paxalom stood looking down at the bleeding, frostbitten body wrapped in its muddy rags, then very quietly he said, 'She has obviously suffered dreadfully because she loved you, my son.' He turned hurriedly to hide his tears.

Slowly Serena opened her eyes and blinked. She was not aware of the splendour that surrounded her – she simply saw two kind and oddly similar faces looking down at her. 'We must have arrived at last,' she murmured drowsily.

'Yes,' said the prince, 'and this is my father, Paxalom.'

She fumbled in her pocket and brought out the tattered little heart, still frozen, and stained by all the other painful things she had endured.

'I brought you a present,' she said shyly.

King Paxalom held it in one huge hand, and this time he could not hide his tears. 'To me,' he said softly, 'this is the greatest treasure anyone could ever give to me. What could be more precious than a heart that is ready to endure so much, simply for love?'

'Thank you for trusting me,' whispered Michael, as she smiled up at him.

'You said it would all be worth it when we got here,' she said, 'and as soon as I saw your father's face I knew you were right.' And, closing her eyes again, she drifted off to sleep.

The Knights of the Octagonal Table began to cough politely, just to remind the king of their existence, so he went back and sat down on his throne. 'Come here, my son, and tell these noble knights why you think this girl is worthy to be their future queen.'

The prince said nothing – he was too tired to think.

Sir Marmaduke coughed again, and shuffled his feet. He had hoped for a grand lady with a large dowry. Sir Roger thought one of the magnificent wax princesses would have done perfectly. And the other knights all had well brought up relations who would have been far more suitable than the ragamuffin on the couch.

So King Paxalom answered his own question: 'In my opinion, no one is worthy to marry my son, and no amount of riches or beauty could give any woman the right to do so, but it is *his* love for this girl and *her trust in him* that is her only plea. And that is definitely good enough for me.'

Sir Marmaduke and Sir Roger smiled at each other, and the other knights couldn't help clapping. Then they all hurried away to plan the grandest wedding celebrations in history.

Hinds' Feet on High Places

by Hannah Hurnard

A beautiful allegory dramatizing the yearning of God's children to be led to new heights of love, joy and victory. This is the story of how Much Afraid escaped from her Fearing relatives and went with the Shepherd to the High Places where 'perfect love casts out fear'.

Let this classic of Christian literature encourage and inspire you on your own journey towards high places.

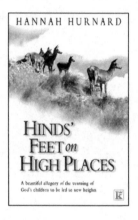

Kingsway Publications

The Father Heart of God

by Floyd McClung

Does God care for people today? What is he really like?

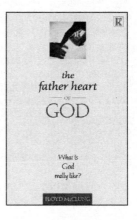

Floyd McClung's bestselling book is a classic introduction to understanding the character of God and his love for us.

Over and over again it has been the discovery of God as Father – perfectly reliable, unlike any human parent – that has brought healing and freedom to many trapped by emotional scars and fears.

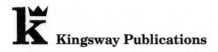

Kingsway Publications